# A Hea

# Journey

## Healing the Body, Mind, and Spirit

Bryony Best

Paperback: 978-1-7392860-2-6

eBook: 978-1-7392860-3-3

Cover design by Aethrastic Designs


Editor Lucie O'Donnell

www.bryonybest.com

# Dedication Page

I dedicate this book to all the souls in pain, who have, or ever will be.

A special mention to the following warriors....

Brand

Caroline

Gemma

Stuart

Jack

Glenda

Mandie

Claire Bear

Mercedes

Pam

Dandies

Sherry

# Chapters

# Introduction

The trees swayed majestically like they were dancing to soft music that only they could hear. Secrets poured out from them in waves, crashing into the stone brick wall of my garden. Energy rooted down into the ground, an electric spark with immense power. I am a tiny ant in existence, an insignificant blob in history, we are all so temporary. I can feel the grass beneath my skin, itchy and pointed like a thousand soft blades waiting to attack on her command, she is watching, observing as she beats down on my skin with a relentless heat. Is she permanent? She is after all the mother of this planet, a force that can give life or take life, she holds the power, and it is she who decides. As Mother Nature rises up and shows us her glory, her magnificence in her divine we are reminded that we are the odd ones out, we are the circles inside a life full of squares. We have invaded and conquered like an infestation, a virus that is arrogant with no acceptance of the effortless flow of energy. We could all ride the currents and move in unity but we choose not to, we choose ignorance. A gentle breeze tickles my skin, soft and playful. The winds of change, I welcome you. I invoke the element and plea for it to take away my pain, my sins and my dark thoughts. I wish for her to whirl around me while extracting negative energy, freeing my soul and releasing me from past habits. We can learn and grow embracing changes and a new direction; we only have to open our hearts and minds to the possibility. Do we truly hold the power to become someone new, to rid ourselves of past traumas and karmic energy loops?

We are more powerful than our human brains could ever comprehend, we are spirit. We are the light, equally as powerful as the sun. Our thoughts are alive, they move and they create building our world around us.

What do we spend most of our time thinking about?

A Robin is sat on my rotting wooden table, still wet from an earlier shower of rain. Many believe that a Robin represents a loved one who has passed over to Spirit. I notice that the Robin bird hardly flaps its wings; instead it rides the waves of wind and gravity. By utilising nature and the elements around it, effortlessly the bird glides and lands upon my shed roof. Nature has learnt how to work as one, in harmony with this planet. Energy is the fabric of existence, transforming and evolving. My body is energy, although it may not feel like I have any on some days, especially when the pain is too much for me to bear.

I am not a doctor or a psychologist. I am a holistic therapist who lives a life of mindfulness and wellbeing. I am well known as a person of experience, after battling common health issues such as trauma, addiction, anxiety, depression, psychosis, nerve damage, and irritable bowel syndrome. The first time I had dark thoughts and considered taking my own life was at the ripe age of eleven. Let's pause for a moment while we breathe and repeat that age in our mind...Eleven.

I have been diagnosed with both incurable and temporary conditions, some physical, few psychological... but all unwanted. I can name many other conditions that you may be familiar with, severe back pain, degrading muscles, aura migraines, chronic urinary tract infections, stomach ulcers, food intolerances. A few of my health conditions were brought on by other problems, for example my alcoholism and drug addiction definitely impacted or was the root cause of my stomach ulcers. You have chosen this book because you are seeking knowledge and answers, can we really impact our own health beyond medical science?

Are there alternative ways to aid our own healing?

In this book I vow to share with you my experiences and knowledge.

I have baffled doctors and experts on many occasions, with my ability to overcome multiple traumas and afflictions.

I am not a gatekeeper.

I am privileged to share my life with you, I hope that you can gain some insight into how I have battled my psychological demons and yet I still manage to live life positively with my long-term medical conditions.

# Chapter 1

# Bryony

I am a Spiritualist, a fiancé, a step mum, and a bad friend who has lost most of hers because I work way too much. I can be obsessive and controlling, and borderline psychotic at times. I am a human-being who is not perfect, but is anyone?

I love my dog fiercely and I am my most happiest when I am in nature. I spend both too much and not enough time watching the trees, listening to them. My many siblings have birthed many children and yet I have never brought life into this world. I neglect my family greatly, I only hope they know the importance of what my neglect means. I work myself into the ground and save every penny, manifesting a brighter tomorrow. There has never been any money or luxury in my family, but I hope to change that for them one day. I currently have five employments, not leaving much time for celebrations or fun. I live in Hayling Island with my partner who works a stressful job for the Government. Steven has Multiple Sclerosis and works full time; he also drives over 150 miles a day to work and back. Most days when I wake up, the first thing I do is to check and assess my pain levels. If I awake to a pain level between one and four then the day may end well, if my pain starts at a six or seven then my day ahead may not be the best. Have no illusions I am not cured of all of my health conditions; I manage them on a day to day basis. Most people in my situation or Steven's may not get up for work, instead they may decide that the pain or condition is simply too much.

My most recent condition is my back and neck pain. I have degrading muscles in my back and neck as well as osteoarthritis. My pain was manageable until May 2021 when a driver crashed into my stationary car, unsettling an already bad condition. After treatments and intervention my condition started to return to my normal pain level, however in December 2021 a severe car crash between several cars on the motorway exasperated this. I have been clean of drugs and alcohol for many years. I first attended rehab in 2005, after relapsing many times I finally broke free of my addictions. I still get the urge to drink alcohol but not because I need it physically or emotionally, I mainly miss the social aspect of it. For me the key to success was to fix the problem of why I drank and needed to escape reality. I was first diagnosed as an alcoholic at the age of sixteen.

My mother still lives nearby, and my father died when I was twenty-one years of age. I have a few sisters who live further north in the United Kingdom but most of my siblings live in Hampshire. I was raised in Portchester and Paulsgrove before moving to Portsmouth where I spent the next fourteen years of my life. I was born in Portsmouth and I love the city dearly. I was a troubled child who fought and acted out at school, with a strict home life. I lived with my two older brothers, workaholic mother and alcoholic father. My mind was disturbed from a young age, even though my father was a Catholic this was not enforced onto me. I heard voices and had visions; my dreams brought me predictions in life that usually came to fruition. I possessed a keen sixth sense and intuition that I later learned was the gift of clairvoyance. I was in therapy by the age of thirteen, an alcoholic by sixteen and a drug addict by the age of seventeen. It seems demeaning to use the word troubled but my teen life was chaotic and gruesome. By my early twenties I was experiencing depression, anxiety, psychotic breaks and psychosis. I experienced stomach ulcers and I vomited blood regularly. I drank alcohol and swallowed narcotic drugs daily, I was also no stranger to red and black blood in my stools. By the age of twenty one I had been rushed to hospital for a suspected drug induced heart attack, by twenty two the doctors wanted to section me in a mental institution. The following years for me were spent living in terror, while having hallucinations and extreme paranoia. I could not determine what was real in this reality.

I wouldn't change a thing about my life, the good, the bad or the ugly. It is a combination of all my experiences that has moulded the strong and wise human that I am today. Remember what I said earlier, I am not perfect. We are always learning and evolving. I do not claim to be a doctor or a person with all the answers, but I do have insight into some specific situations. It was my approach and spiritual knowledge that aided my healing and stopped me from being sectioned into a mental institution in the past. I was previously assessed by a doctor at Cavendish House, who was blown away by my healthy approach to many of my life experiences. It was this doctor who decided that even though he had no belief in Spiritualism, he prescribed that I should attend a

Spiritual Church for a short time before being reassessed. This was the moment that changed my life completely. A journey unfolded before me that led to self-discovery and knowledge that changed me forever and set me on a new course.

*"The real magic is not hidden in a magician's hat, it is what is living inside of you." – Bryony Best*

## Chapter 2

# Trauma

Have you ever experienced trauma?

What is trauma?

Trauma is an event in our life that was deeply distressing or disturbing. As we are all different and perceive the world through separate eyes, ones experience of the same situation can be varied greatly. For example, if a person who has experienced a generally trouble free life then a relationship breaking down or the loss of a job may seem traumatic to them. However to a human who has battled through many trying situations, they may deem a job loss as a simple blip. Trauma can affect us in different ways; it can sneak up on us years later. And like a punch to the gut it can knock the wind right out of us. Obvious symptoms can be instantaneous for example, shock, denial, or a change in behaviour. Each person's ability to process and respond can vary, some people may become withdrawn or have suicidal thoughts. A sudden panic attack, phobia or medical condition may present itself that the person has never experienced before.

After a traumatic childhood I turned to alcohol and drugs, escapism from my experiences. My most recent car crash has also given me a fresh fear of driving, after my first car crash, I did not drive my car for a few months. This time I chose a healthier approach to help my fear, by accepting support from doctors in the form of CBT - cognitive behaviour therapy. I also let the tears flow every time I spoke about the latest crash, and the pressure of being a driver for a vehicle that nearly resulted in the death of five of my family members. The crash was not morally or legally my fault yet I felt guilty. Each time I closed my eyes I replayed the horrific crash inside my mind. I let my imagination run wild, fantasising possible alternative endings. My mother crying with my sister Vikki while my family wept for the lives lost. I had my sixteen year old nephew Tru in the car, his older brother who was twenty one and my heavily pregnant niece. I can recall my fear like it was yesterday, it is still fresh in my mind. The shock as the vehicle behind plummeted into my car at over sixty miles an hour. How I felt when I opened my eyes to find myself facing oncoming traffic on the motorway. The speed in which I responded, pulling up my hand-break and pressing the red triangle hazard button. My first thought was to film the crash for evidence, after being hit from behind only a few months earlier I was more prepared. I am ashamed to admit that it took twenty seconds before I looked back at my smashed up car in concern for my family members. The eldest nephew could not move to exit the car, and when I spotted my pregnant niece clasping her stomach and her head as she struggled to get out of the car, I felt sick. Reality hit me that she could be in serious pain, or that harm had come to the unborn baby. I have accepted that the crash was an unfortunate event, while being grateful that we all walked away from the wreck alive. I often meditate and ask for healing from the earth and universe, drawing up strength from Mother Nature. My spiritual guides give me healing and I receive healing energy via crystals and holistic therapies. I will share my knowledge on trauma healing with you, but first I feel it is important to tell you about a few more of my experiences that I categorize as traumatic.

I lived with my brother Brand for many years, as children and again as adults. We were like two peas in a pod, our values and thoughts often mirrored each other. My heart exploded with the love it carried for him, it often felt as if we were two halves of the same coin. He has never really smoked or had an alcohol or drug problem, unlike me. Some may describe him as a fitness fanatic, because he was always at the gym and was selective of which foods he put into his body. I can remember the day he dropped the *C bomb* on me, it was outside Queen Alexandra hospital, and I had just left after being booked for an abortion. I had fallen pregnant and the doctors said it was an ectopic pregnancy. I have never wanted to have children, which was convenient considering that I was diagnosed at the age of seventeen with polycystic ovary syndrome and low oestrogen. I was twenty eight years old when I first started falling pregnant, it was a complete shock to me but I still did not want to raise children. After multiple trips to the hospital they finally pushed the paperwork in front of me to be signed, with scary possibilities of various surgery complications. I fled the hospital in a flood of tears, that's when I bumped into Brand and his girlfriend Rachel. She was wearing sunglasses and had obviously been crying. I assumed they had been arguing as there was an awkward feeling in the air between them. As we walked to Rachel's car in silence my mind rushed through random worries and concerns for my operation booked for

Thursday. It was a Tuesday and the sun was unusually warm for the time of year. I could feel the hard concrete beneath my feet as we paused next to her car, birds chirped and sang their songs mockingly. Brand lifted his chin high and informed me that he had cancer........ His biggest concern was that he needed to inform his employer that he may need a few days off work, because his surgery was booked for Thursday. My heart thumped so strong inside my chest it felt like it may split me open. Blood rushed to my ears increasing my internal heart beat song. Pedestrians walked by without even taking a glance in our direction. My mother had taken Brand to the GP as a child and he was diagnosed with a descended testicle, which I believe is pretty common amongst boys. Over the last few years Brand had found it difficult walking but he never missed a day off of work, instead he had sought help via his GP surgery. They pretty much dismissed him, on one occasion when he was sent to the hospital for his groin pain they had sent him away with an estimated diagnosis, a guess if you will. An incorrect guess it seemed, because a year later he walked into the same hospital and left with a diagnosis of cancer. It was this knowledge that alerted us to the fact that he may have had this cancer for years, but due to an overstretched NHS or negligence, he had been delayed a diagnosis. Brand was torn between surgery booked for Thursday and a trip of a lifetime planned for a flight to America on the same date. He decided to take his holiday even with the cloud of cancer hanging over his head. I attended my own surgery and he waited for his operation booked for a future date. They removed his testicle and he returned to work one day later, against doctors orders. He needed the money for bills and rent. He attended scans regularly and we were informed that his type of cancer was 99% aggressive, they called it Teratoma Cancer. Brand adjusted well and continued life as normal, I too soon stopped feeling like a stranger had invaded my vagina after my evacuation. The real pain was yet to come; it was twelve months later that Brand telephoned me while I was teaching a class at work. He never called me during work hours so I swiftly exited the building to receive his call. I was stunned into silence by shock as I listened to his news; he had too received a call while at work from a doctor. He had been informed that his scan showed signs that he had cancer tumours in his back, and maybe in his lungs. I couldn't believe that they had this conversation with him via telephone, who would deliver such life changing news via a phone call! Against my normal behaviour, I left work immediately and demanded to Brand that he too leave work for the day. We tried to seek more information from his doctors but with no luck. At this time in my life I was working as an Employment Coach full time, I also worked in clubs on odd nights. I facilitated a Development Group for Spiritualism and taught Kickboxing to local females for fun. My time was stretched and on top of it all I had recently started my own children's entertainments business with my closest friend, Mercedes. The next few years consisted of chemo, operations, possible loss of organs and life. My brother was in pain and lost many things that he loved. His hearing loss was a great loss to him, as a musician he loved to play his guitar, piano and drums. I was juggling multiple jobs, a new business and all while trying to support my brother. His girlfriend Rachel changed her whole life to move in with us and to support him as much as possible. We were all sadly affected in so many ways; the good news is that he is still alive today. In his darkest hours he would question the powers above.

"Why me? Why has this happened to me?"

It was a good question, if anyone deserved the cancer then surely it should have happened to me. I had taken drugs for years, abused alcohol and smoked cigarettes from a young age. I said to Brand "Children and babies are diagnosed with cancer every day, they surely do not deserve it either. One day we may discover that mixing certain chemicals causes cancer, or self loathing is what causes it. Until we discover the physical or energetic reason for cancer, all we can do is fight".

Brand did not give up, he fought tooth and nail to return to his fitness and to get back to his version of normal. I am glad that this experience is sat quietly in the dark, on a back burner at present. He will never be cancer free and he continually has scans and appointments but for now it is not in our face as it once was for many years. Brand received treatments and surgeries for his cancer and also spiritual healing from above. Throughout this time I concentrated on supporting my brother, offering him energetic healing with the tools at my disposal. I am a Spiritualist therefore I offered him healing, which he accepted openly.

Another traumatic experience for me was when my dearly beloved niece, robbed me. She was the apple of my eye, she could do no wrong. I doted on her and spoilt her in great measures. She was my world; I protected her and defended her. I guided her when it was needed and shared my wealth of knowledge too. She wanted for nothing, as I would buy her pretty things and eagerly give her my money. It was a shock when I noticed funds were going missing from my bank account, but that shock was nothing compared to the day the police informed me that they had caught my niece on CCTV. She was withdrawing money from my bank account. I was furious with her; I was hurt and felt betrayed. How could a person rob their own family? I was a great aunty to her, and everyone knew it. Why steal money when the person freely hands it to you? These questions bombarded my mind minute by minute, and hour by hour. I was heartbroken, I sat inside my room and took a lot of drugs to numb the pain but there was not enough Jack Daniels in the world to block out the hurt. I carried it with me like a heavy sack of potatoes. The pain it caused me being betrayed by my own flesh and blood, my darling Kayleigh. It nearly broke me. There are only a few years between us, I am her aunty but in reality we were best friends, sisters, mother and daughter, teacher and student. I was always the one who was the adult and who looked after her. The truth is I am only three years older than she is, yet the dynamic was as if thirty years separated us in age. As an angry person I gave her two options, to face me and take a beating or to leave Portsmouth. She decided to leave. I carried that pain with me everywhere I went, it changed me temporarily. It was years later that she returned to Portsmouth and started to send me money to pay back the thousands she had taken. We were not friends or family anymore, just a victim and her betrayer. After some time had passed my niece was attacked while walking down Victoria Road South, a man had attempted to rape her. Luckily a neighbour had heard her scream and they said there was something different about the sound of her voice. Being a busy road the residents are used to screams and laughter from drunken teens and adults. Kayleigh had been on the telephone at the time and although the attacker was not successful she escaped but with minor cuts and bruises. This resonated with me, as I once had been drugged in a local bar and an attempted rape was made on me. Unfortunately for my attacker he was not aware that I had a high constitution for drugs and alcohol, so I managed to fight him off. Stupid man, for at the time I was pretty much having sex with everyone who crossed my path, it was the date rape drug that angered me. A cord was struck and I forgave my niece for her indiscretions against me, but it was not just this that led to my forgiveness. I believe that we are spirits in human form having a physical experience. Therefore we are in this body and life to learn and to grow. We choose our parents and generation to engage with in this world. As do we select many of our life experiences and lessons to be learnt. Of course there will be unplanned situations because as humans we have free will, which also explains why terrible things can happen in this world. If humans were not given free will then it wouldn't be life at all, if all bad experiences and decisions were taken out of our hands then we would merely be puppets or actors. I eventually understood that I had chosen that lesson in the spirit world, and if the person closest to me needed to betray me in order to fulfill that experience then Kayleigh was less of a perpetrator and merely a pawn.

*"It is through pain and anguish that our greatest lessons are learnt." – Bryony Best*

# Chapter 3

# **Loss**

My father died in 2005, I remember the year well.

I had recently left an alcohol rehabilitation centre and it was a few weeks later that we were informed of his death.

Grief can affect us all in many different ways. I myself can recall when my Granddad died, locking my bedroom door and playing the songs Bed of Roses and Blaze of Glory by Bon Jovi on repeat. Many humans are lucky to not encounter a death until they reach adulthood, with the loss of a childhood pet being their only experience with death. My father's dad died before I was born, so I unfortunately never met him. My father told me stories of his achievements and I would stare at a black and white newspaper clipping, imagining what his voice may have sounded like. My Granddad from my mother's side passed away when I was eleven, I recall feeling sad and I used the emotion to compose a poem. At the funeral held on the Isle of Wight, I watched in sadness as others attempted to speak at the service. They all failed. I vowed to not let myself cry and to be able to share my words with the crowd. I did it, sob free. I finished my poem and had managed to find the strength from somewhere deep inside me. I was not as close to my Granddad compared to my sister Vikki or brothers Arren and Elijah. Brand was invited to attend the service but he declined, while Vikki sank a bottle of vodka before she had even left her flat on the day of the funeral. My brothers helped to carry the coffin and they held their heads high, not a tear in sight. My mother was devastated and spoke of taking her own life later on down the line. In the years to come I would catch her staring into a framed photograph of my Granddad, while crying and shouting obscenities at me for hiding any pills that we usually kept inside the medicine cabinet. I felt sad for a few weeks but for my sister and mother, the hurt lasted for many years. When the opening line of the song - *Wind beneath my Wings* would play on the radio, they would both sob like his death was only yesterday. Maybe I adjusted better as I had been forewarned of his death, I dreamt of my Granddad rocking a baby in a graveyard. Nearby was a pub in darkness, the lights were on and I knew others were waiting inside for him. Not long after my Granddad had passed away, a boy in my school died too. I was not friends with the boy, nor did we interact much. Everyone in our school year knew that he was ill, yet he never looked unwell to me. A parent should never have to bury their child, and even as a young girl I understood this saying. I stood at the back of the young boy's funeral, with many other pupils from my year. I pounded the concrete beneath me as I walked away from Portchester Castle, I felt confused. I couldn't understand my feelings and thoughts, so I asked my friend for one of her cigarettes. I had previously given up smoking when I started secondary school, as everyone always assumed I was a smoker. I never liked living up to their expectations or to be predictable. What I did know is that death wasn't the end, that an afterlife existed. It wasn't long after this that I lost a close Grandmother figure named Dot, once again I had been given a dream to warn me of her death. She was the sweetest lady with kind blue eyes, white hair and a short plump frame. I remember feeling a great sadness but it passed quickly, she had already lived a full life and had died peacefully in her sleep. Somewhere between the age of twelve and sixteen my Great Grandmother died too, along with a close friend of the family named Toni. My Great Grandmother was very old and Toni had been terminally ill for some time. My experiences with death remained silent for a few years, bringing me to 2005, when I was twenty-one years of age. Turning twenty-one is a great milestone for many, for me I was heartbroken and mentally unstable. I was an alcoholic and a drug addict too which didn't make my future seem full of hope. Instead I was overflowing with anger and resentment, my light was broken and I could not shine. My father's death was inevitable like all of our parents. I still think about being a child wrapped inside his long coat, walking along Portchester shoreline. He would share stories with me that I was far too young to hear. Yet I understood them, he taught me many valuable life lessons. He was a very intelligent man, who was talented with singing and football. I never truly let myself grieve for him, I was too angry at the time. I must have been in shock when I was informed of his death, as the next day I turned up to work as normal. It was a manager who noticed my behaviour and she questioned my wellbeing. Now I must have been acting strange for them to notice, as they were usually exposed to intoxicated me who acted pretty weird on a daily basis. We had missed the funeral, so I later travelled to Ireland with my mother and Brand to visit his grave. So, there I was twenty one years of age, freshly out of rehabilitation and my father had died. I am not a cold person but once again I soon bounced back, besides my life and mental health being in a shocking state, I survived. My father is not gone forever; I often speak with him and my Granddad when I meditate. What I have not shared with you is the loss that has affected me the most. Some may assume it was a shocking death in 2013, my close friend Jack. I have just read through the last few messages that we exchanged on social media, Jack was definitely one of a kind. He was misunderstood, partied hard and drank too much. He was too young to die, and I only met one part of his puzzle. I never attended his funeral. I couldn't bring myself to go. We were so close, yet I cannot recall even half of our time together. We shared secrets and snuggled on the sofa; we slammed shots and took ecstasy as friends do. I met him while working at a call centre in Portsmouth; we were both fans of escapism, two lost souls. Our friendship formed fast and we spent many nights together, painting the town red. Jack was unpredictable and fiery; he had so much personality and was the life and soul of the party. His eyes are what gave him away; for me it felt like looking into a mirror. Eventually Jack moved away and he deteriorated, sinking further into the bottle. We spoke via telephone and months later we met up, when I was at the start of my recovery from alcohol and drugs. This stage was a very delicate time for me, filled with mental health issues and urges to drink myself into oblivion. It was hard to be around him, he was a reflection of me that I didn't want to see. He was the match and I was ignition. We were no good for each other, so I backed away when he needed me the most. I feel sadness for this but I had to put myself first. He was soon committed to the Bluebell Ward for his mental health. He would call me to chat but his communication was aggressive and at times he just rambled. He was certain we were supposed to be together; he called me his She-rah. He said he had found investors for us to open a nightclub in his home town, but eventually we would move it to Alcatraz Prison. When he died, a mutual friend named Lisa had tried to call and inform me, unfortunately my mobile phone had been stolen at my new job. I was spending my days between work and QA Hospital, so I did not find out immediately. I know he is in the spirit world looking out for us, and no doubt causing havoc up there. As sad as all these deaths are to me, they are not the end of their story. Their spirit lives on and they will inevitably return to this earth plane and leave the essence of who they were in this lifetime up there. I am certain of this, at times I wish that death did mean the end. If I had even the slightest doubt that the end could be true, then I would have taken my life when I was eleven years old. If I had survived childhood with that belief, then I certainly would have committed suicide when I was in my teens or early twenties.

The greatest loss for me is the relationships that we have lost, my loved ones who are still living yet I can no longer share their life with them.

Whether you believe in an afterlife or not, a person who is dead does not feel physical pain. If you agree there is a heaven or spirit world then you know they are in a better place. So who are we really grieving for?

- You – and this is completely expected, and acceptable. We will never stroke their hair, hold their hand or witness them age on this earth plane.

*"Do not stand at my grave and weep. I am not there. I do not sleep." - Clare Harner*

# Chapter 4

# Pain

The word pain can refer to many types, from physical to emotional and psychological. If I break down my life into sections of different pain it would look something like below –

5 years of age  +    – Emotional

13 years of age +   – Psychological

28 years of age  + – Emotional

32 years of age +    – Physical

I find it very interesting to draw a timeline and then add important or life changing moments. Mapping out pain and patterns can be a useful tool when seeking answers to which negative impacts or environments have affected oneself throughout their lifetime. The pie chart of pain represents my own interpretation of my pain, as a child I felt emotional pain from my home life. Living within a household with an alcoholic father brought its own set of issues. I do not include the physical and painful punishments that I received throughout my childhood. I do recall the fear that would creep up my spine, before crawling into the pit of my stomach when I heard that awful sound – a sharp, quick slapping noise caused by a leather belt being snapped in half. My father would walk up our staircase while creating this fearful noise. My brain would calculate whether the thrashing was coming for me or one of my siblings, on any occasion when it was for me I would cower to the end of my mattress. As a petrified child, I would crouch on my bed for safety while hugging my body against the corner wall, while hoping to be able to convince my father of my innocence. My heart would pound so hard that I believed it would explode, yet it never did. My grey bedroom door would slam open and there he would stand.

The Shadow Man.

Loudly I would scream and shout "No daddy, please, no daddy".

Like a mother holds both ankles of a newborn baby when changing its nappy, he would swoop my legs up in the air and then .....WHACK.

I usually deserved the punishment and within seconds it was over, I would gingerly retreat to my pillow and cry until my tears would flow no more. The physical act of being whipped with a leather belt was fleeting; it was the torture of knowing it was about to happen that usually got to me. I do not feel sorry for myself as I do not feel I was hard done by as a child. I also do not feel any animosity towards to my father for what he did to me, I am sure he felt the punishments were suitable. I am a great believer in the old saying - "What doesn't kill you only makes you stronger". My father made me strong. He did have other forms of punishments that I did not care for, one being suffocation and the other involved a wall. We would be forced to lean all of our body weight against a wall via our finger-tips; we were then instructed not to move. Eventually the weight would cause severe pain in the fingers leaving two options. Option one was to stay exactly as you were until your fingers gave out resulting in your face planting hard into the wall. Option two was to concede and face the punishment that he deemed fit. You may find it interesting that I disregard any childhood physical pain from my pie chart but this is because it was short lived, temporary. The emotional pain, which was both on-going and a daily occurrence, was where the true darkness slept. I recall sitting in class at Wicor School wondering what the evening would entail. There were weeks when things were quiet and less drama filled than others, but like waiting for a kettle to boil, the drama would overflow and erupt like clockwork. We never knew exactly when it would happen but it always did. Some of the predictions were obvious, for example on pay day or benefit pay out day. The cash would be too tempting and my father would go away and not usually return until his money was spent. Sometimes he returned with plasters on his arm, which he would usually explain to me as being a Band-Aid from him giving a blood donation. On other occasions he would return with what looked like a red circle around his lips. As an adult I now know the blood donation was police enforced whenever he had been caught driving under the influence of alcohol, and the red circle was caused by constantly swigging from a bottle. When I share memories of my childhood with others most people are shocked into silence, accept for my closest friend Mercedes or my siblings. The big debate is nature verses nurture; I do not believe that all abused children will become abusers. Just like I do not agree that all deprived children will become criminals or thieves. However it is obvious to me that our childhoods, home life and environments play a big part in shaping our minds and ones understanding of the world.

Have I ever whipped a child with a leather belt? No.

Will I ever whip a child with a leather belt? No.

Will the child of an alcoholic become an alcoholic themselves? I did, yet my siblings did not.

The difference being that I eventually fought my demons and I am sober and clean, living a healthy and positive life. I also became a drug addict yet I never witnessed my father or mother swallowing narcotics.

The length of pain plays an important factor, for short term pain can be handled well but long-term pain can be debilitating. I was only able to escape my addictions when I faced the true cause of them, and it was not medication that helped me if I am honest. As a teenager I did try taking tablets and I swallowed them all in hope for a miracle. The source of one's pain is where the release can be found. I struggled for many years with psychological and emotional pain that led to anxiety and severe depression. They were dark days indeed, I turned to narcotics and the devil juice to cope with life as the pain of living was too much to bear sober. The alcohol and drugs barely masked most of my issues, and they brought a suitcase of other problems to add to my already over weight carry on. I contemplated suicide on many occasions. I am glad that I never followed through on them. My mental health was battered and I was usually hanging on by a thread, for years I was tormented and felt so lost. From the age of twenty one I was a mess, addicted to alcohol and drugs. The following years were pure hell; I was trying to kick my bad habits which meant I needed to heal. In order for me to heal I needed to find the source of my pain. By the age of twenty one I had gathered so many traumatic experiences it was hard to know which one was the true source to my pain. My biggest step was to truly give up the alcohol and drugs, I gave up the drugs within a month or so but the alcohol had its claws in me so deep that it took many years for me to truly be released from its vice grip. The million dollar question is; what actually helped me release all of my demons and allow me to heal? The answer is knowledge and enlightenment, now before you throw this paperback or your kindle towards the wall just stay with me for a minute. If you strip back trauma and emotional pain, at the root of it all is confusion. Why did that person rape me? Why did my parents beat me? Why was I born into a violent house-hold? How could that friend deceive me? Why did that lover cheat on me? It is the question of why and the lack of understanding that can torment us. We will never truly understand the actions of others, especially if we would never make them ourselves. So, how did I gain enlightenment and knowledge for my own traumas? I meditated and I asked for guidance, I sought knowledge and surrounded myself with deep thinkers and people who were interested in the evolution of human kind and healing. I returned to the spiritual church and investigated holistic therapies and natural remedies. I learnt about Reiki and Spiritual Healing, the power of Manifestation and the importance of balancing energies. In the United Kingdom we have the NHS and as part of that healing service they make referrals to alternative therapies. Scientists and Holistic Therapists may agree partially and disagree often but are we open minded enough to investigate and so we can make our own decisions? Yes! I discovered that we are energy and beyond the typical human eye is a force at work that we can either flow with harmonically or against to our own detriment. Consider radio waves, you cannot physically see them flowing through the air but if we tune to the right frequencies then we can listen to that wave. Now for a moment consider that nature, humans, souls, animals, plants, trees, elements, and everything we know is energy. Our thoughts send out energy, so therefore we can communicate on a level naked to the human eye with the universe, shaping our reality and future. Do we have the power to heal our body, spirit and soul? Yes. We are not great believers without instant gratification. However, if you truly understand that all far and wide is energy including ourselves, then yes, we can affect everything! I use this knowledge to balance my energy and to work with harmony. This does not mean I never get angry or shout or swear, but I am aware of my energetic flow and how to use nature and holistic therapies to release negative energy, expel trauma and to heal. Did I heal my mind within one day? No. Did I heal my traumas within a few months? No. However, with every day and week that passed, my symptoms retreated slightly. This continued until I reached a healthier state of mind. I used all of the energetic resources around me to heal my body, mind and soul. I understood at my very core the answer to the million dollar question of – Why? The answer does not matter; it holds no secret meanings to you or to me. Most humans that act in a negative way do not understand themselves or why they do what they do. Humans must be given free will to make their own choices, so this answers the great question of why would God or powers above allow bad things to happen. Maybe my lesson to be learnt in this life can only come from experiencing true pain? The earth plane has rules similar to a computer game, so therefore some bad things can simply be a result of cause and effect. There is no MAGICAL answer; there is no GREAT meaning to the WHY. There is the experience and the lesson learnt, we can use this knowledge or we can let the question of why drive us to insanity.................

I understand this completely and it has set me free, I am not claiming to not feel pain or loss or grief - I am simply explaining why it will never break me. Once I truly accepted all of my past experiences for what they were, I found a peace that allowed me to move forward and to progress.

*"Pain is temporary, pain is guaranteed. Love is eternal and love heals all." – Bryony Best*

# Chapter 5

# Long-term Conditions

My most recent pain is the physical kind, the long-term pain that can have me laid up in bed unable to even turn my own head. My physical pain is dragging and testing, I have days when I can cope and other times when I cannot. I can blame my pain on a couple of things, my addictive personality which led me to exercise and push my body until breaking point. I can also blame my recent car crashes; yes I think I will blame them. I previously injured myself and my back has never been the same since, from trapped nerves to degrading muscles and slipped discs, or the time I overstretched my ligaments before kickboxing and I popped my hip off of its alignment. Add a car crash to the mix and we have a seriously injured back and neck, throw in another more serious five car smash up and boom – welcome to permanent damage. Two car crashes make for a confusing law suit so the red tape left me for over a year with no treatments, resulting in delays and even more unnecessary pain. I am not the only one; I have many friends who are fighting long-term conditions from Fibromyalgia to Multiple Sclerosis. Then we have the big C, my friends with Cancer who would swap positions with me medically in a heartbeat. The bottom line should be that if we are in pain then it means we are alive, however try saying that to someone who hasn't slept in weeks and has lost all the joy in their life from their disabling and painful condition. I still suffer with my stomach conditions too which can range from severe stomach cramps to consistently vomiting. I find blood in my stool often and in my vomit too. According to the internet blood coming out of either end is a serious medical emergency or at least a reason to seek medical advice. In reality it is not treated this way, well not in my experience. Interestingly I was offered an injection many moons ago, one that would take away all of my pain. It sounded too good to be true, and it was. The catch being that they would only offer me one injection, it would only last for a few months, so what happens after the pain relief injection ceases to be effective? All that pain would come crashing around me again, and I would be back in my swamp of daily pain management. I did consider the offer for a few moments but it was fleeting. What mental turmoil would that have had on me?

To be released from my years of hell and to exist in a world where I am not in constant pain, only to be returned to it? I decided that to enjoy the relief from my pain and to experience a life of freedom, would be knowledge more incapacitating than the conditions themselves. You may have chosen the option as a positive one but I did not see it as suitable for me. You may be thinking that a few months pain free should be welcomed with open arms, I strongly disagree. I have lived with my medical conditions for so long, that I have forgotten what it is truly like to live pain free. To be reminded of a pain free existence only to have it cruelly snatched away, would mentally set me back. At the present time I am functioning well for a person with multiple medical issues. Many people who are diagnosed with long-term or life-long conditions usually can enter a stage of depression. I wouldn't expect anything less, especially if one can no longer enjoy their hobbies, partake in exercise or work in a job they have trained their entire life for. I was unable to eat at a friend's house or sleep over a gentleman's house for many years, due to my stomach condition. This also affected travel, so holidays were more stressful than one person should ever have to experience. My mental health would also take a battering at the thought of becoming ill while being stuck in another country. I once had a psychotic break while aboard and the idea that it could happen again still scares me to this day. I used to love kickboxing and running, football and contact sport. I can no longer partake in these activities. The fear of going on holiday petrifies me and my fear usually convinces me to either cancel or to not book one to begin with. My body physically changed shape when I was advised not to continue with my exercises; the real fear was that my lack of exercise could affect my alcoholism. I swapped one addiction for another, when I was giving up the alcohol I turned to sport and exercise. All these anxieties plagued me like demons, shouting loudly and drowning out any of my rational thoughts. If I go to a restaurant for one of my friend's birthdays, would I make it back home before an IBS attack would start? If I board an aeroplane and my stomach kicks off will I be stuck and embarrassed on the small toilet? If I carry my own shopping bags will my neck pain kick off making me unable to work tonight? If I am taken to paradise on a ship, will I lose my marbles and have a psychotic breakdown? Could I be committed to a mental institution in another country? These questions were not irrational for it was many real life experiences which scorched the memories into my mind, reminding me of the possibilities and my own fragile state. Anxiety is another demon that can drop by when a long-term illness roars its ugly head, as every new physical condition births different outcomes and possibilities. Do not blame yourself if you are unable to make plans previously agreed with friends, and do not give two hoots if you have to cancel on an agreement to protect your own health. If your family and friends cannot support you and they openly do mind helping you when it is needed then I say – "FUCK THEM". I mean it in the politest way possible, do not waste time asking the question of; why can they not support your medical condition, instead just release them. Maybe they're not strong enough for the challenge or maybe they are just not that into you! A simpler answer could be that their plate is already full and you are just too much for them. Stop worrying about the fact they are not making room for you on their golden plate and accept the situation for what it is. I had to shed many relationships when I stopped the alcohol and drugs; I also lost many so-called friends too. It is interesting that some friends responded to my sobriety with negative comments, questioning what would I drink if I was in the pub with them? Will I still be going to the night clubs? Can they still drink if I am around them? My favourite response was from one of my closest friends; Mercedes – "If you're not drinking alcohol then we will just have to meet for a coffee". I can always trust and rely on her; she is a true friend and a loving soul. Stress can affect all conditions especially pain, so it is important to reduce stress or have some tactics for keeping yourself calm. I have found that by knowing my limitations and accepting them I can work with my pain. There is a big difference between knowing your limitations and respecting them. I avoid heavy lifting at work and at home, I also do not carry out manual handling duties. When I am working at my main job these limitations can be very constricting and put pressure on others. At home I do not clean my house or vacuum it either, this may sound like heaven to some people but to me it is another form of hell. I hate germs, I detest dirt and I was brought up in a spotless household where everyone chipped in to keep it immaculate. The cleaning now falls solely to my partner Steven, who also has Multiple Sclerosis and he still manages to work full time. He once lost the majority of his eyesight which I believe is common with his condition, luckily after a few months it slowly started to return but not all of it. Part of his condition is extreme fatigue and his legs and back hurt from his nerve issues. Sadly his eyesight has definitely decreased over time and his cleaning standards are hardly near my high expectations. Poor Steven has to clean the house, and he does this with a spring in his step just to keep me happy. I have tried cleaning one room and then taking an hour break and so on but this did not stop me from shooting past my exertion limit. I wish I could clean my own house but guess what? You do not always get what you wish for, so we had to find a new way to adapt and cope. I find as my back and neck condition has worsened I can no longer wear heels; well it is a good bloody job that I don't really go out anyway then. Why do I not go out anymore? I can cope with my pain and function, but throughout the day I worsen and therefore any night-time antics are simply out of the question. I also take medication early evening for nerve damage which can make me drowsy. It would appear that a long-term condition can strip away most of the joy in one's life and leave a boring, coping plan for day to day functions. I am a responsible adult so therefore I prioritise being able to leave the house for employment, I may be a spiritualist, but I still have rent and bills to pay. If I lost my home and was sleeping on the streets then that really would muck up my back and neck. No one wants to be homeless; we all seek security and stability. Human beings thrive when they are safe, loved, have purpose and support. You do not need to be educated to know these simple things, so my employment is at the top of my list. Some flower sniffers may say that happiness trumps all, but I wouldn't be very happy or stress free if I was evicted now, would I? The start of my pain journey was very different to now, many years ago I had a high level of pain but I pushed through until it broke me. Now in the present, I work around my pain and push it with minimal effect to ensure a slow progression rather than a detrimental regression. Before I accepted and respected my new conditions I was consistently breaking myself, regularly taken in and out of hospital, to the GP or chiropractor appointments with serious injuries. Now I still go into hospital and to the chiropractor but to work on a continued healing and progress plan. I am slightly happier with my progress now, it may be slow but it is measurable. I may not be able to attend the gym or a kickboxing lesson but I have recently returned to swimming. I am not a fan of the chlorine, and neither is my hair or skin but hey ho, beggars can't be choosers. I take pain medication before and after a swim and I force myself to take breaks between my lengths. My new exercise routine may not be exciting but guess what? I am doing it! For the last eighteen months I have not even been able to stretch out for a few minutes without my pain peaking to breaking point, now I am the little mermaid swimming twice a week. To recap I have shared with you that it is important to respect your new limitations, do not waste time on yesterday's capabilities and instead, live in the now. Release friends and family who cannot support you. That does mean you cannot remain friends or in a relationship with them but do not let any bitterness bubble away and eat you up from the inside out. Be prepared to adapt and to overcome, find new ways to complete tasks and or new hobbies if that is what is needed. There is no point in sharing my opinion on medications or tablets as I am not a doctor or your doctor for that matter. My final secret to impart with you for pain management is to share my rituals and routines. What do I do that I find helps me the most? I practice mediation and self healing, using Spiritual and Reiki energy. I also read as many books as humanly possible with my work commitments. I find that when I am reading a book time slows down. The clock is always against me, I am often stealing a glance at Big Ben to see if I am late for the next task. Yet when I am holding a paperback in my hand or swiping an e-book on my kindle time becomes my friend. Giving myself time to read and to get lost in someone else's world, transports me out of my body and to a new place entirely. I am sick to death of hearing my friends say "I don't have the time to read". I want to scream in their face "I have five fucking jobs, I work seventy to ninety hours per week. What the hell do you mean you do not have the time?" I could rant for days about this subject but I won't, instead I will remind you; how can we ever have time if we never take time? The same can be said for exercising, yes I know I was obsessed with it but going to the gym or for a morning run is a choice not a matter of having the time. Get up an hour earlier, or go to bed an hour later, trust me you won't regret it. My brother Brand still managed to make time to exercise when he worked twenty-nine days a month, and he worked twelve to eighteen hours a day. Brand even worked out at the gym when he had cancer; there is no excuse – just choices. Meditation and healing helps me greatly, it reduced my stress levels which helps with my pain. I ask my guides and spiritual helpers for healing and I visualise a green light engulfing my body. The beautiful and warming green energy is welcomed with open arms as it travels into my energetic field and fills my aura with healing power. I visualise the energy is moving like water, washing over my elements, and releasing any negative energy and freeing any pain or illness. The cabin in my back garden is filled with the most precious crystals and I use them for balancing my energy and to heal myself too. I stand on the grass and ground myself, I connect with the earth's energy and let her power pulsate through me. I avoid strong pain medications due to my past addictions, choosing a holistic approach to my pain management. I do take a nerve medication in the evenings and over the counter pain medication on the days that I go swimming. Doctors and professionals will usually recommend meditation to help with long-term illnesses and pain. Obviously, I eat a healthy diet, but it does not matter as I have intolerances to nearly ALL foods. I do not drink alcohol or take narcotics. I listen to my body, when it tells me I need a break I try and take one. When my body twinges in a certain area it is literally communicating with me. Listen to your body, what is it telling you? If you have never meditated before you can access many guided ones via the internet or you could even approach your local Spiritualist Church if you wanted to receive healing, it is usually at a cost of a small donation and performed by volunteer healers.

Why not join an Awareness Group or Development Group in your area; you could learn how to heal yourself and others? I am only sharing my truth with you, this is my story and what I have found helps me. I used to facilitate my own Spiritual Development Groups and offer Mediumistic Readings to people; I later navigated towards the healing side of Spiritualism. Pain is important as it is a clue and it tells us a story however too much pain all day, every day is never wanted.

Pain can keep us safe; it can remind us of dangers and near misses. Pain can help us to avoid hazards and life threatening situations whether physical or psychological.

*"Pain is plentiful, and is an unwanted companion for most. Pain is essential and can be our friend, don't let it hold you down in the dark." – Bryony Best*

# Chapter 6

# Anxiety

Anxiety is similar to a side order of crispy french-fries, because it comes with everything! Depression and anxiety, now they are a common duo, just like stress and anxiety as they love to walk hand in hand too. If you find a person who has experienced trauma then you will usually spot their good friend; anxiety. Apart from phobias which are generally tied up in knots with anxiety, I notice how other conditions are generally a trigger or cause for anxiety. If memory serves me correctly I think doctors refer to it as a secondary symptom, in other words it is not the main cause. You can be literally crippled by the condition and it has a ripple effect, washing over your entire life like a pond of dirty water. It clings to you and ruins everything. When people tell me they have suffered with anxiety for many years my response usually shocks them. I nod and make positive noises; my body language can be baffling also, until I explain myself to them. We all know anxiety can be short term and go away when the main factor has been treated or fixed, but in reality most people endure long-term anxiety. So, when I am informed that a person has already reached many years of suffering I feel positive that they could soon be coming out the other side. Mine lasted for a short time as a teenager, but when it returned to pester me as an adult, it lasted for many years. I, personally believe the length of the condition all depends on the cause and one's journey to heal? I have already shared with you a snippet of my past experiences, however despite my childhood, I did not display symptoms of anxiety when I was a child. My first experience with anxiety hit me like a tidal wave, crashing me into the hard rocks and spraying my life into the wind. I was twelve years old when it happened, of course, I did not realise at the time what the correct name for the medical condition was with me only being a child. My mother used to set the video recorder on a timer to tape all of her shows onto a VHS-Tape, for those of you that are too young to remember – you can Google it. My mother loved to record *Prisoner Cell Block H* as it aired at silly o'clock in the morning. She tape recorded a few other shows too, on this occasion I had knocked her video recorder remote control down the side of her bed. I quickly reached my hand down between the bed and the wall, replacing the remote control exactly where it had been before I had knocked it. A terrible feeling bubbled up inside of me and my mind swirled with unrealistic possibilities. My eyes were wide with fear and I felt as if my heart would explode. I knew the thoughts and outcomes I was contemplating were ridiculous, but I had no control of my mind, and my entire body was shaking, while I was screaming high pitched gibberish. My brother Brand and father witnessed my outburst and afterwards I ran to my bedroom for safety. I had no idea what was happening to me, but I kept having these wild thoughts about my simple everyday actions, I would convince myself that someone who I loved would die and it would all be my fault. To my mother I was acting normal and carrying on with day to day activities, but in reality I was having a complete meltdown. Another memory that springs to mind is when I played with Brand's miniature swords. He had a tiny display that several swords hung from, I think he got them from a charity shop but I cannot be certain. We were living in Washbrook Road in Paulsgrove and each room had its own gas fire attached to the wall. I held one of his swords which were smaller than a pencil, and for no good reason I poked it into one of the metal-grid gaps of his bedroom fire. The next few moments consisted of my mind playing scenarios of the house catching on fire from a gas leak, and it being my fault. My solution was to let someone else take the blame, so I called out for my father to join me in Brand's bedroom. In my scared state I convinced my dad that I thought I could see something in the fire place behind the metal-grid. I then casually passed him a sword to poke into the fire in search for a foreign object. My father soon gave up after poking around and then left the room, but the fear and panic never escaped from my body. For the next few days I attended school but I couldn't eat. My brother asked me why I was giving him my lunch every day but I never shared my problem with him. When the panic and fear started to take over my life I tried a new tactic. Every day I would tell my mother about when my father poked a sword into Brand's fire and that I feared we would die in a gas explosion. Eventually my pestering worked and we moved house, to Cheltenham road in Paulsgrove. It was bizarre, but I believed in all of these irrational thoughts, and it drove me to be in a consistent state of worry. The thoughts could be ridiculous but I was unable to use my experiences and knowledge to chase the dark thoughts away. I remember placing a chunk of blu-tack on a wall once and that one simple action resulted in weeks of worry. It was hell. I was like a prisoner inside my own mind and a slave to my dark thoughts and worries. My panic attacks and anxiety only lasted several months or so, but it was pure hell. It was not until many years later that I was diagnosed with anxiety and depression in my late teens. I was prescribed medication but reflecting on it now, my alcohol and drug taking obviously contributed to the condition. Underneath all of my symptoms were twisted traumas that were rooted inside of me, growing vines that presented as many different illnesses. When I was not high on drugs or sedated with copious amounts of whiskey, is when the anxiety would roar. Walking down the street was similar to walking through a forest of nightmares. I believed most people were going to attack me, or were conspiring against me. My behaviour was unpredictable and often I would have an outburst, shouting abuse at others who were simply walking down the street. My drug addiction and alcoholism masked my anxiety and panic attacks for many years as a late teen and adult. I lived in a vicious pattern of depression and anxiety; this in turn caused me to continue swallowing street drugs and alcohol which fed the anxiety and depression. My anxiety reached its peak or was more noticeable when I was slowly withdrawing myself from my addictions. All my issues and tissues that had been buried were now floating on top of the surface, big, bold and ugly. I accused a guy who I worked with of putting poison into my moisturiser cream. I also shared this accusation by pointing the same finger at one of my house mates. I thought my house mate was also putting something into my shower-gel, to cause me mental confusion and illness. I was desperate for answers and felt this possibility was sane and plausible. I believed I was being poisoned by different people; as they were trying to make me ill. I believed that no one could possibly feel the way I did, unless someone was doing something sinister to cause it. I started seeing black spots when my anxiety was high, my body would shake and I would feel sick and dizzy. My symptoms were so extreme and my fears were so out of control that I was like a bomb waiting to explode. My doctors did not help me, as I was a registered alcoholic and drug addict. I turned to the Spiritual church, seeking healing whenever the opportunity arose. My irrational thoughts had returned but they were mainly paranoia, which spread like wild fire and no one was off limits. Everyone was the enemy and all humans were a threat. I once laid on a toilet floor inside an airport, in sobs of tears while refusing to catch a plane back to England. I felt so sick, dizzy and paranoid. My mother at the time tried to comfort me but I was a mess. I used to fly as an adult to visit my mum when she moved to France, but my anxiety ate me up and spat me back out, I crumbled under the pressure of going abroad with my illnesses. I recall telephoning my sister Vikki, while I was travelling to Southampton airport to catch a plane. I explained that I was very ill but I was booked onto a flight, I then made her promise to make me an appointment at St James Mental Hospital for when I returned to England. Vikki kept her promise and I was assessed at St James, the diagnosis was Psychosis. I refused treatment as I feared the tablets would stop me from exercising, I would have rather been skinny and insane than chubby and sane. How I tackled my anxiety symptom was through meditation, I was given a CD that was specifically designed to open up the suggestive part of the brain. I listened to that CD several times a day, and I kept exercising which I found helped with the adrenaline which caused my body to shake. I lived in *Flight or Fight* mode, which caused stomach issues and shaking. If unchecked, this made my paranoia and anxiety worse. If I had an attack during the evening I could sometimes still my mind by reading. Many occasions I would still be flicking through a paperback book well into the sunrise. The tools that helped me the most were; meditation, exercise, spiritual healing and reading. The biggest impact was of course to overcome the main cause of my issues. Whether the addictions or traumas were the main cause did not matter, for they both played their part. It took many years of personal growth and sobriety for me to heal my old wounds. Healing can be messy, it is painful and ugly but ignoring these dark elements and burying them deep down is like painting over mould.

*"Like a rotten piece of fruit, hiding at the base of a bowl, emotional trauma will spread and inflict decay."*
*– Bryony Best*

# Chapter 7

# Gut Health

Do you know what I call a person who can eat anything their heart desires and then not end up having a love affair with a toilet bowl?

**Lucky!**

No one likes to talk about it but we all poop, yes even us females. For many people, they have the pleasure of not giving food a second thought. For others like me, I have to plan and monitor all food that passes my lips.

Let's talk about shit!

WARNING – the following may contain content that some readers may find; puts them off of their food!

In this chapter, I am going to share with you some disgusting, inside information concerning *Irritable Bowel Syndrome.* If this sounds like too much information then you can skip to the next chapter. For those of you that are still reading, I will also share with you what I have tried and tested over the years to help ease my symptoms. Before we jump straight into the deep end of the toilet bowl I would like to point out; that everyone is different and the following chapter is my experiences and my own truth. Travel back in time with me, to my teenage years when I could eat anything and not put on several pounds at the sheer thought of eating a cake. The first sign that I ignored was when I was roughly twelve years of age, each time I had a sachet of *cup-of-soup* I would end up on the porcelain throne. My first experience happened while working at my mother's charity shop in North-End. I was crippled over with severe shooting pains in my abdomen and my body felt as if it may rip into two. Sat on the toilet in absolute agony was then accompanied by hot flushes, so I was forced to strip off all of my clothes. Being blessed with long hair also required me to hold it high up high, off of my neck and shoulders. The attack would last anywhere from several minutes to half an hour, but within the eye of the storm I truly felt scared. I never told my mum about this and I soon forgot about it. I was never aware of food intolerances at that age and I didn't think to monitor my attacks. Between my teenage years and early adult life I was used to my new normal. A bloated stomach that was tender to touch or a sickly feeling after eating a meal was often expected. I never sought medical help at the start, over the next few years I also became an alcoholic and drug addict, so I did not pay much attention to my stools. At the ripe old age of sixteen I did seek help from a doctor; I was experiencing severe pains in my upper abdomen and lower back. I was diagnosed with a stomach ulcer. The doctor at the hospital also informed me that I had done severe damage to my liver from excessive alcohol intake before my organs had finished growing. It was only later on in my twenties that I noticed the blood in my poop. I know black blood can mean upper GI bleed and red blood can mean lower GI bleed. It is not uncommon for alcoholics to have blood in their stools. I would vomit when I did not drink alcohol, this usually occurred on an odd occasion when I would give up the alcohol (which would only last a few hours at best). My vomit progressed to also having blood speckles within it, again this is common too. It is fair to say that I am not the best witness to recall how my stomach condition was progressing between the age of seventeen and twenty five. I can only be honest, if we fast forward to when I first left Nelson Clinic; a rehab centre for alcohol and drug addiction. It seems hardly fair to rob you of all the details but my recovery was a bumpy one, full of relapses. However each gap between the relapses slowly increased until eventually I was addiction free. In the early stages of my recovery I was eating healthier food and exercising. I was constantly at my doctors surgery begging for help, I was bombarded with what I felt were new symptoms. The fact was, I had been masking or sedating many issues and medical conditions with my intoxications. I discovered that when I ate food I vomited multiple times a day, my stomach always hurt, and I was not a happy bunny. My doctor explained it was a secondary symptom caused by anxiety. He said it would gradually go away but it did not. My brother Brand suspected that I had an eating disorder because he overheard me vomiting several times a night. It wasn't until he ate dinner with me one evening and watched me dash towards the kitchen sink to projectile vomit everywhere, that he was convinced otherwise. I had not pushed my fingers down my throat or forced myself to be sick, I had no control of it and he witnessed it firsthand. If I ate certain foods I would also end up in the bathroom with excruciating stomach pains and diarrhoea. After months of this, my doctor finally referred me to the hospital for a consultation. I was instructed to keep a food journal, which I did and this showed that I was pretty much intolerant to most foods. But a girl has to eat, so what was I to do? My stomach issues caused me anxiety, plus my original anxiety because I was sober caused my stomach condition to flare up, so I was stuck in a loop of permanent pain, vomit and poop. As a result, I became obsessed with what food I ate. I monitored everything and started counting fat content, as high fat foods had a worse affect on me than lower fat food did. I avoided going out for meals, or eating at work and I couldn't see any end to the torment and darkness. This was certainly a stress that I did not need on top of being sober; but I was eventually diagnosed with IBS. I was advised to take medication to stop the bowels from contracting. I found the tablets useless as they did not really work for me, plus my bowels were trying to eject the food not to slow down the process. Years passed and my condition only worsened, which forced me to send off samples for testing. The results confirmed that I have intolerances to EVERYTHING, including healthy food. My trigger foods were; high fats, sweeteners, onions, potatoes, strawberries, seeds, nuts, apples, and a long list of ingredients found in nearly all food products. The stomach condition added to my fear of flying, and still to this day it affects me. I refuse to live in a house with only one toilet, deeming it as unacceptable. I have had many terrible experiences relating to my IBS but I will share just two with you. In 2015 I started a children's Entertainment company with my friend; Mercedes. We were the first company locally who offered superheroes and princesses to attend kid's parties. I was stood on the stairs of a popular venue in North-End dressed as a princess from a beloved book and film. I held a basket with roses attached, filled with gifts and books ready to read to the children. Inside the party were over thirty excited children who couldn't wait to meet their beloved princess. I had opted to not eat a thing which is what I do when I need to be certain to avoid a vomiting or poop attack. My stomach grumbled just as I was about to walk inside and pain crashed through me. I rushed to the toilet while wearing a fluffy big dress, and had an attack right there and then. I was stuck inside that toilet with the sound of screaming kids outside the door, in the middle of an IBS attack which caused extreme pain and sweating. Twenty minutes later, with my body shaking from pain and shock, I exited the toilet, plastered a fake smile on my face and continued with our party booking. The parents kept asking my business partner if I was okay when I was held up in the toilet like a hostage, she just smiled and explained that the dress was very big and difficult to manoeuvre. I had been referred to a specialist who I met for my first consultation, followed by my second appointment which was over one year later. After having a camera shoved up my backside and a camera forced down my throat, I was calmly informed that my body is just different to other peoples and that I would have to live with the condition. Just an FYI - the same camera was not used for both investigations!

At that point in time, I was vomiting after nearly every meal and I could pass a stool up to twenty-three times a day, a specific number I know. I have that number burned into my brain, as I pleaded with the doctor to find an alternative solution to help my condition. I cannot apply for certain employments because of the condition; I avoid eating throughout the daytime and opt for eating predominantly in the evening, when I return to the safety of my home. I have tried the gluten free diet. I have eaten only one type of food for thirty days to see how that affected me. I have literally starved myself, other times I have only eaten foods with low fats. I stopped eating junk food. I ate pro-biotic food and yogurts for gut health but none of it cured my condition. My latest embarrassing experience was in Scotland, meeting my partner's father for the first time. It took many years of planning and convincing for me to agree to the trip. While they ate fried breakfast I only allowed water to pass my lips, when travelling through the beautiful mountains I starved myself while they feasted on burgers and steak. My plan was working, I was hungry but it was a small price to pay. On one of the trips, we ventured afar to visit Loch Ness and it was beautiful. We explored Urquhart Castle and the views were breathtaking. On the way back to his father's house we stopped for food, I listened with jealously as they ordered delicious juicy meals. I was feeling brave and ordered a ham sandwich, I know, crazy right. I felt a twinge in my stomach half way through munching the sandwich and I dashed to the bathroom. It was both a noisy and busy toilet which is dreaded by all IBS sufferers. I sat on my throne of hell, shaking in pain, sweating like a waterfall and the poop just wouldn't stop coming. I was panicking that they would wonder where I had got to, my phone confirmed that an hour had passed yet I was still not able to leave my new hell. In a state of horror I ran toward Steven and announced "I need to leave. NOW!" While gripping my abdomen and bent doubled over in pain I crawled into his father's car, red faced from embarrassment and wishing the ground would open up to swallow me whole. His house was only a few miles away but I had no hope of making it that far. I needed to poop and I needed to do it immediately. I groaned aloud and shuffled on the backseat while praying to god to not let me shit in his dad's car. I was mortified and as soon as we pulled into the driveway I ran to the guest bathroom where I spent the next few days! No-one wants to hear all of my sad poop stories but trust me I could fill a book with them. So, after all these years I still have severe IBS, so what knowledge can I impart to you?

The number one trigger that affects IBS is stress. I still avoid eating at work or when going out for the day. I choose to eat when I return home in the evening, however I also find that stress and anxiety are the biggest causes of an IBS attack. I have certain red flag foods, which are big ones to avoid. A few examples would be; Take-away foods, sage and onion stuffing, certain fruits and white bread. I have been taken to hospital on a few occasions relating to my stomach condition and each time the doctor has suggested the removal of my appendix. I always refuse the surgery and so far I have been okay. I can have attacks that last weeks, with no sleep or rest. A few years ago I was taken into hospital several times for suspected stomach ulcers; they just pumped me with pain meds and increased my prescribed Omeprazole. I have found that by decreasing anxiety and stress I can try and decrease my attacks. I know my limitations with food types and I stick to them. I use techniques for healing by asking the Spirits above for help, and I meditate too. All of these tools help me to stay balanced and offer me longer periods of decreased symptoms which I am able to cope with better. I also joined some online groups for support and this brings me great comfort, if you are similar to me you will have spent hours unable to leave a toilet while scrolling through comment boards on the internet searching for answers. I could easily use this medical condition as an excuse to throw in the towel, to give up. If I vomit while I am at work, I simply wipe my mouth and get back to it. If I have a mini IBS attack at work, I wash my hands and crack on with my tasks. We can choose to either take control or to let the conditions take control of us.

I choose life.

*"What goes in must come out." – Bryony Best*

# Chapter 8

# Doctor Love

I would honestly prefer to refrain from talking about love, not because I do not enjoy the topic but rather because it reminds me of a sad time in my life. I would like to assume that everyone has felt love either from their family, friends or a significant other. I have luckily enjoyed the feeling of love from my parents, siblings and friends. I have also fallen head over heels in puppy dog love, while walking on air, surrounded by beauty. All love is different and in many cases not guaranteed to be eternal. We wish we could find our soul mate and be captivated by the sheer beauty of the mushy feelings entailed. We can survive without love, but it is a sad existence without it. I have a tiny, angry Chihuahua that hates everyone. She is my world; I would die in a heartbeat to save her from feeling any form of pain. Animals are a great comfort; maybe you have a cat, dog or ferret? My friend Gemma; cares for her guinea pigs better than some parents take care of their own offspring. Care homes and hospices often have animals visit that are trained as pet therapy animals, they give us so much joy and in return they ask for very little. We can learn a lot from them, if you are ever feeling sad or sorry for yourself then watch some videos about three legged dogs. They have no anger, resentment or loss. The furry animals find a new way of living; they simply adjust and continue with their life. I am wise enough to admit that if I lost one of my legs, I would definitely sit and dwell on my own pain and loss, like when we lose a loved one from this earth plane. My grief would take over, it would take a big adjustment and I am unsure how I would cope. Dogs are like these bountiful balls of energy and love, they are angels to us humans. I am not implying that my dog can fly or partakes in cloud surfing, but their everlasting love can heal and save souls. It would appear that love from animals is also included in my list of sources of love. We cannot force ourselves to love others, similar to how we cannot easily stop our love for another either. I have felt true heartbreak from losing love in the past, not just from partners but from friends and family too. My most recent being one of my nieces, she is a troubled soul who is denying me her love due to her own anger and resentment of me. This hurts me deeply, for I have taken care of her for many years, I cannot force her to forgive me or to love me. I would be happy just to know what the reason behind it all is, a mystery that taunts me in the late hours of the dark night. I would guess everyone has felt the loss of love, with a string of tears reserved for the truly big losses like death. When a relationship breaks down it can be very painful, your stomach can feel like its twisting and our lungs can tighten with the absence of oxygen. Similar to grief, we can feel numb, sadness, anger and trauma. The loss of a future we previously envisioned with another, the warmth, or touch that we may never experience again. I am ignoring the other side of the coin, when a toxic relationship ends, as the ship sinks to the bottom of the ocean allowing you to resurface and to finally enjoy an intake of breath. I witness my sibling turn to the whiskey to replace the warmth of his wife, after a long relationship it crashed into a bitter ending. My brother could not simply switch off the love that he had for their partnership, only finding comfort in drowning his feelings with the sharp sting of sour bourbon. I too let myself become lost in a negative relationship when I was a teenager; I carried my own heavy baggage that allowed my eyes to be blind to any truth. At the ripe age of seventeen I fell in love. The relationship was toxic and volatile, but I felt that I could not live without him. I too increased my alcohol and drug intake to numb the pain after it ended; I was in a black hole that was ready to suck this world into my void and to let myself be swallowed with it. For many years I was a mess and it is only years later that I can honestly be enlightened to the truth. It was not the relationship that saved or ended me; it was me, myself and I. It was a combination of factors that made me vulnerable, open to manipulation and danger. I could write a separate book detailing my journey through that terrible ordeal, I didn't care whether I lived or died and this was obvious in my self-destructive behaviour. I was selling drugs, taking drugs, downing bottle after bottle of whiskey and chasing danger like a stuntman. At the time I blamed everything on the loss of a partner; it was a little more complicated than this. So, what is the healthy way to get over a loss of a partner? In the past I tried numbing my pain, forgetting about the problem. I even slept with hundreds of men to wipe away the memories of him and replace them with new ones. I asked the Spirit realm for healing; I even approached a psychic medium for advice. Nothing I attempted worked, I was falling down off a cliff and sadly I had no wings. After my eight year experiment, it was apparent that sex, drugs and rock and roll were not the answer to healing after a relationship had ended. Time did help as the old saying goes, time heals all wounds. In my case it did help but it certainly did not heal me completely. I am glad that it didn't work, as giving others the advice of an eight-year plan that involved alcoholism and drug taking is not really the healthy option. What did kick start my healing was when I began working on myself; I do not mean analysing my faults or ensuring I picked up clothes from the floor. I eventually started to take better care of myself; I reduced my alcohol intake and stopped swallowing illegal drugs. This was the first step for me, it was hard work and painful but what I was truly doing, was making a choice. I was choosing life. I was picking me to come first, to be the priority. When you decide that your life could be better, or you decide that a situation is no longer good enough for you, this is the start of something truly magnificent. When you consciously decide to pick you, and to make yourself a priority this is called, self-love. To love oneself is not selfish, how can we hope for another to love us if we are not even aware of our true worth? You may have witnessed or experienced a time when depression takes over and a person neglects their hygiene, refusing to shower or even brush their teeth? Self love and knowing ones worth is the complete embodiment of healthy. My steps to improving my health for my body, mind and soul was a positive step in the right direction. My day would start with an early morning run, followed by a swim at the local pool before I went to work. My food intake changed from take-away junk food to fish, vegetables and low calorie foods. I was feeding my body with the correct foods and working on my physical body too. I had much healing to do, so therefore the next few years consisted of a healthy routine, and I was a regular visitor at my local church of spiritualism. I asked for healing from the church volunteers, never forgetting my own personal responsibility to aid my healing journey. I meditated and practiced healing on myself, using visualisation techniques to aid my process. All of my new habits combined together strengthened my core and this resulted in my mind being able to evolve and gain insight into the past relationship that once caused me so much pain. With a new perspective, I could see that I didn't lose the love of my life, in reality I dodged a very lethal bullet. I was also able to take responsibility for my actions and contributions to the whole catastrophe. My new vantage point offered me a new perspective of being a learner, I was taught a valuable lesson from the relationship. I am worthy of love, I am whole and complete as an individual. A partner should be someone who can add value to your existence in any shape or form. I should be able to function to the best of my ability without a partner; therefore, if a relationship is temporary or taken away from me then I shall remain standing strong like a mountain. This does not mean that I will never be hurt by another or walk the path of grief, however it does ensure that my walk will be short and not detrimental to my own life or existence. I have many friends who are looking for their significant other; I try to explain the importance of self love first. Another important factor is to remain as a learner, a student of life who is experiencing many lessons. If a child was enrolled in a school that only taught one lesson, then you may question the quality of their education. It is the same in life, it is through multiple lessons that we learn and grow. This theory can be adapted to lessons of love; we cannot expect every partner to be the one, or a true love to last for eternity. Similar to working in a job role, most of us do not start our career as a big shot project manager; we progress and develop through simpler jobs that prepare us for the important role that may be waiting for us to arrive. You have to kiss many frogs to find your prince, and each kiss will help you to grow, learn and change as a student of love. I am not suggesting that you kiss hundreds of amphibians and then slip into your best dress while you wait for Mr Right to walk into your life. I am merely pointing out that yes, we may want to fall in love or to be rich with love but self love is the positive starting point. You cannot wake up each day and simply mutter the words, you have to believe it in your heart and soul that you are worthy and that you matter. Once you truly reach this discovery you will not allow others to take the piss out of you, you will no longer let yourself be taken for a ride. I am not suggesting aggression either, I am talking about YOU being your number one cheerleader, and advocating for yourself. A parent easily advocates for their child, only accepting the best for them, yet we struggle to show ourselves the same level of compassion and love. Step two is the realisation that every relationship and experience is an opportunity to learn and grow. What did you learn about yourself from your last relationship? Maybe you now know that you want more attention or a partner who has similar goals in life as you do. I learnt very early on that I will never stay in a violent relationship, after witnessing too many sad experiences from my sister's life. I vowed to never let myself be a victim of domestic violence. I learnt from my sibling's relationship, similar to how I vowed to never accept an alcoholic as a partner after watching my mother struggle for many years. We can learn from everyone around us, in a positive way of course. Some children will accept what their parents demonstrated as normality or as acceptable in life or a relationship. When I was with my ex-partner as a teenager, the one I previously mentioned, he did hit me on one occasion. I had just returned home after a twelve hour shift working at a restaurant in Gunwarf Quays. He had been drinking vodka with his friend, and I was angry to find him and the house in a mess. I became enraged and shouted profanities at him, when out of nowhere he punched me in the face. His fist managed to strike me so hard that my bottom tooth pierced through my lip line. He was a tall man and much older than me, I was nineteen years old when it happened. I took the punch well, even with the obvious height and size difference. I had experienced many street fights, including altercations with fully grown men. I wiped the blood away from my lip and dashed straight to the kitchen. In my anger I selected a large, heavy frying pan and I attacked him back. He was six foot four in height and I was five foot seven, so I used a weapon to even the odds. By the time I started to attack him, he was already on the floor as his best friend had punched him in the face as punishment for hitting me. His friend was much shorter than I am so he was brave to strike him. I hit him repeatedly, bashing him over and over. Like a good citizen, I then took him to hospital where the staff questioned us both, assuming we had been taking drugs. I calmly explained that I was still in my work uniform and sober. I pushed him out of the hospital in a wheelchair, and he never laid a hand on me again. I have many friends who have survived domestic violence, and their stories did not end as shortly as mine did. Maybe I was just lucky to have been an experienced fighter, or to have an explosive anger issue that aided me at the time. I believe that I have learnt from all my experiences the good and the bad. I cannot offer an answer that protects you from emotional pain or from ever being hurt. I can offer you an insight that can make those types of experiences when a relationship ends, to become more positive or meaningful. An experience is something that has happened in the past, the word experience implies the time frame of temporary. There are not many experiences that are permanent, so with this knowledge we can accept an experience as a short term situation that offered an opportunity to learn and grow. Obviously there are some situations that may be too painful too approach with this mindset. A good example would be rape or murder, it is hard to not see that type of experience as anything other than negative or detrimental. However, with time and healing, even painful and heart-wrenching experiences can be healed and accepted as temporary. We may not always be able to erase the fact that a terrible experience was thrusted upon us, but we can choose how we respond to said situation. Mindset is a fascinating topic; it can make or break you when living through challenging times. We may not be able to control which experiences we have in life but we can control how we respond to them. - Now that is very empowering. Love is the Holy Grail in life, if we feel love whether it is from our pets, family or friends then we are richer than we could possibly comprehend. Love yourself, and then you will be at your peak to love others.

*"True love that is guaranteed for eternity is the love that you give to yourself. Love that you give to others can echo through the ages. Choose life, choose you."*

*– Bryony Best*

# Chapter 9

# Anger

**To be consumed by anger is devastating to our quality of life.**

I have been a victim of this on many occasions, although to call me a victim is far from the truth. The word victim implies that anger was done to me, when in reality anger is an emotion that we feel or experience. Emotions can be involuntary and if left unchecked, can rupture like a volcano burning anyone who gets in its path.

I have experienced feelings of anger on many occasions; it is common for others to refer to my explosions as an Irish Temper. I can fly from zero to boiling point within a split second. I am a work in progress and on no level do I pretend to be perfect. I am unfortunately a person who is either perfectly okay or walking towards a situation with a can of petrol ready to burn everything to the ground. As an adult, I remind myself that each human is learning and growing, and that it is better to turn the other cheek and walk the high road. The egotistical side of me plans and plots my revenge, concocting devastating ideas of the most severe way to inflict punishment onto an offender. I am aware that I do not sound very mature or enlightening to share this truth with you, but I did promise you honesty and I never promised you perfection. Hopefully you have never travelled the ugly realms of hatred, burning with fury and fuelled by darkness and evil. Big words to use but in reality they are just avoidance, a way to distance myself from any past behaviours. If I use biblical words or scary descriptions then it almost gives the impression that a higher or lower power was casting its wand and forcing its spell upon me. I was once diagnosed by a doctor of having a *God complex* and he also added that I was *dangerously over-confident*. I am sure this was a fair assessment as I believed I was quite rightly the judge, jury and executioner. Teachers from school described me as being violent with an aggressive nature. I was raised to hit back, to defend my honour. If I returned home from school with a blackened eye, you could bet your bottom dollar that the other kid returned with two. In my teens I was often in environments that required me to defend myself physically, I have lost count of how many street fights I have been involved with. A scarier statistic is the fact I have had more fisty-cuffs with men than I ever had with females. I would never have described myself as an angry teenager and god knows I had the right to be. I was raised inside a violent house-hold with a poor upbringing and an abusive home life. I watched my friends live a normal childhood filled with holidays, presents and picnics. We once sat in the cold on a wooden bench at Portchester Castle, the rain poured down on us while we ate Polony sandwiches. That is the closest memory I have to a picnic or family day out. Other children worried about whether they would get invited to the latest party, while I stared into space wondering whether my dad would drink all of our money away? I never felt bitter or jealous of my friends, how can a child wish for a better life when the reality of their circumstances was all they had ever known? As a teenager I came to realise that I didn't have much in common with most children my age, so I distanced myself from them. I would often listen to their chatter at lunch time, investigating and soaking up their normal problems absorbing them in like a sponge. I felt like an alien, watching a different species who liked to gossip and talk about boys. I do believe that the other children must have known something wasn't quite right with me, I recall a girl named Lucy speaking loudly with excitement to her gang of mates. Her eyes were wide and her grin was large as she told the others how she had seen me smile from across the bench. It was such a big deal to her and she has probably long forgotten it, yet I can never forget that innocent comment. I accepted my life for what it was; drama filled and dangerous. My true anger was born when I was drowning in pain from a relationship break-up. As I mentioned earlier the situation is more complex than what has been explained so far. I often fantasised about killing the child who my ex partner was dating. I also thought about killing him too. These were not fleeting thoughts but honest plans to commit murder. I had so much rage burning inside of me and I believed that torturing the ones who had wronged me would help to ease my pain. My darkness spread as easy as warm butter does on toast, soon latching onto my brother's wife. She too had betrayed me and what started as a black seed of hate grew and developed into a new obsession. When I lay in bed at night I pictured her tied to a chair while I inflicted torture onto her, this simple act of fantasising gave me great pleasure. I dreamed about hurting her, cutting her eyelids off and sticking metal under her fingernails. I would hammer spikes into her skin, slowly but deep. If reading this is sickening to you, then please forgive me and move forward to the next chapter. I thought about this when I was awake, when I was asleep, while walking to work or sat on the bus. I was consumed by these thoughts and I had no escape from them as they plagued me day and night. I know it is wrong to hurt another, I am also aware that it is illegal, but this meant nothing to me, nor did it deter me from my plan. When my anger was at its peak, I lived with my best friend Jane, and I talked incisively about killing Janine. By the way, Janine is Jane's mum! In an attempt to cause this woman the most possible pain imaginable; I considered the option of shooting my best friend in the face just to spite her mother. The loss of my best friend seemed a worthy trade to hurt this woman who had scorned me. I would drink bottles of alcohol to forget the pain or to numb my feelings, but underneath all that anger was hurt. I was echoing to the planes above, waves of my pure torment and anguish. For years I was stuck in a negative cycle, a loop of eternity like Groundhog Day that I was destined to endure forever. My anger was literally killing me, the whiskey fuelled my rage but it often comforted me too. If you have ever experienced an anger that is so dangerous it morphs into an obsession then you will know how consuming it can be. I wasn't aware of it at the time, but I was only hurting myself, it was me reliving the pain and allowing myself to live through my darkest moment time and time again. I know that this woman wronged me, but does that really justify a punishment of death? I found some clarity somehow, and I forced myself to focus on all the good things Janine had done for me throughout her life. She had been a loving lady when I was a child; she fed me when I played in her house. When I was homeless and living in an empty abandoned flat, she welcomed me into her home. Janine took me shopping and cared for me when I was mentally vulnerable as a teenager; she had shown me great love and affection over the years. My first step to putting out the fire in my stomach was to write her a letter; I took acceptance for my actions and explained to her why I had taken her betrayal so deeply. I was far from innocent, for I had lived in her house as an alcoholic, sipping vodka at 6am while ironing her children's clothes. I posted her a condolence card when she announced her wedding date to my brother; I even threatened to shoot the dog that she had stolen from me when my dad died. I never would have shot a dog, but I knew she believed I would. I have always been a firecracker, who could turn faster than a light switch. I still felt betrayed, but eventually I became fully aware that my anger was hurting my family, friends and me. I started to keep a journal, scribbling all of my thoughts to paper. Journals that I hope to god my good friend Mercedes will burn if I should meet a timely death. Writing is a great way to process our inner thoughts and feelings. Many readers ask if my memoir books have been therapeutic for me to write, the simple answer is yes. The more complicated response is that, to dig up past memories is like waking sleeping lions – usually best left alone. Reading a journal offers time to reflect and there is something more impacting when reading a sentence rather than hearing one. Maybe audio book listeners will disagree with me, but I have always found this to be true. I found that by reading over my ramblings I could learn and grow. I included positive statements and affirmations to help me let go of my anger. Visualisation is also a great tool, offering the manifestation of letting go of habits or thoughts that no longer serve you. To forgive others, is not necessarily an admission of right or wrong, but it is a necessity for your own ability to move forward. I have found this to be true in many aspects of life. I did once harbour negative thoughts towards my mother; I blamed her for some of my childhood trauma. It was freeing to realise that no human is perfect and just because a person is your mother or father it does not exempt them from this statement. My mum, like your mother is here on this earth plane learning and growing, like all parents they are only capable of doing *their* best. When you recognise that all humans are imperfect then it is easier to accept their flaws. Once again, some flaws may be small, while others could be violent abusive wrecks. We are not always in control of our own emotions and feelings, never mind trying to understand others. We are not the person who hit us, the same as we are not the friend who betrayed us. We are not the sick people hurting animals or children, but we could be a relative of one. Imagine the pure horror of birthing a serial killer or raising a rapist, it happens. It would be wrong to simplify all acts and to place them all under the same umbrella, but if all humans are trying their best or failing to develop, how can we stay angry with them? I am not referring to murders and rapist or animal abusers, as we can probably assume they are mentally disturbed and sick. If you are insightful, you can usually sift through someone's bullshit and surmise why they act a certain way or why they are the person that they are. Who is at fault, the gossip queen or the person who shared their secret? It is an opportunity to learn who you can trust; maybe you are the one with a big mouth who shared the secret in the first place? Is it possible that Janine hurt me because she was trying to be loyal to another? Was my mother perfect? She definitely was not, but she did the best she could with the knowledge and the tool box that she possessed. A tool box could be filled with love, experiences, and morals, learnt behaviours, insecurities, and conflicts, being unaware, emotional trauma or even pure ignorance. When you look at each person as a student who is still on their path of love and enlightenment, then it is easier for one to move into a position of acceptance. My journals lasted for many years, alongside my love of writing poetry. I asked the Spirit world for healing and support, and I looked within myself to learn and grow. I also found that exercise and kickboxing helped a great deal as it is a healthy outlet for hot energy. Many people with anger issues have reported that exercise is a great tool to help them cope. I have discovered that when I am angry about a situation or a person, it is usually just the straw that broke the Camel's back. I question my fury, why is the person upsetting me and what can I do about it? I have taught myself to respond to situations rather than reacting. Reacting is instant and usually filled with emotion, but to respond requires you to take some time and it requires calculation. I ponder the options of what I would like the end result to be and then how I need to respond to achieve it? Most people do not reach their true desire by punching someone in the face or by screaming profanities at them. Next time that you are in a situation that stirs feelings of anger, walk away with the information and mull it over. Think about your desired outcome before you respond, this always results in a better outcome. Once you reap the rewards of one good outcome you will opt to use this method in the future.

*"Like a disease inside your mind; anger will fester and grow destroying all love that resides in you."*

*– Bryony Best*

# Chapter 10

# Depression

Not the great depression but the other kind.....

If you have ever stumbled through the dark tunnel of depression, then you will already know that it is a lonely path to walk.

I was diagnosed with depression when I was a teenager, this then led to frequent therapy sessions. I suppose a doctor could say that the illness is caused by a chemical imbalance in the brain. Interestingly enough, recent research has suggested that this is not true, with no clear answer for its true cause. Depression can be induced for multiple reasons, so we cannot dismiss the importance of psychological, environmental, and biological factors. One may argue that living in non-nurturing conditions would obviously have an impact on ones happiness. I recently watched a film based on a true story, two unlikely animals were raised together and formed a loving bond. After an unfortunate turn of events, the two animals were separated, with one be taken to live in a circus and the poor animal was subjected to horrible acts of cruelty. The second animal was distressed, missing his companion and finds it hard to bond with his own species at a sanctuary. After a time had passed both animals escaped their new lives to be reunited together, they continued on their path travelling home to where they were raised. It was joyful to watch them play and run free like all wild animals should. It was interesting to witness how the animal from the circus had been affected by his poor environment. He was no longer captured or forced to perform yet he was haunted by his experiences. The empathy that I felt was overwhelming, and I must admit that my eyes watered many times throughout the film. I kept analysing the situation and comparing it to one with humans. When a person endures a tragic or stressful experience, we expect them to heal and return to their normal self. I am not implying that we are heartless, however we may have had a colleague who has lost a loved one, but we still expect them to grieve and then return to work as normal. A child may lose a parent who has been incarcerated for a criminal offence, yet again we expect them to adjust and return to school as normal. This information taught me two things, the first being that I have more empathy for an animal than I have for myself. The second being that I don't always truly give traumatic experiences the respect they deserve. I focus heavily on the positivity of healing and moving forward, that I forget to celebrate and applaud what we humans are truly capable of overcoming. Never in a million years would I assume the tortured animal to be unscathed by his trauma, yet I demand myself to heal almost instantly. I feel it is important for me to remind you that my healing journey was long and spanned across many years. In a previous chapter I shared with you my view on time-scales relating to depression, they can be short-term but are more commonly known to last up to several years. Depression can suck you dry of any energy and motivation, which are two very important ingredients for tackling tasks that can aid you to feel better. A vicious cycle can form when people are trying to dig their way out of a black hole. My depression was originally caused by trauma, but my continued depression was aided by my alcohol addiction and drug taking. Like a butterfly that flutters it wings, a ripple effect is sent out like a tidal wave. Alcohol causes depression and heavy drug taking messes with both your mind and body. These previously mentioned factors do not create the optimal conditions for healing. I will never know whether therapy could have helped me, for I attended many assessments and very few active counselling sessions. I was never offered tools or new ways to cope or deal with my condition or trauma. The doctors fed me tablets while the therapist fed me more diagnoses. I did not notice the tablets affecting my mood for the better, nor did they offer me any improvement. I tried and tested many pills; this was back when patients believed that the right pill could help stabilize our brain chemicals. Quite rightly, I was attempting to heal but failing miserably, swallowing pills to hide a problem while still chugging down whiskey and ecstasy. What did I think would happen? If it wasn't for my alcohol and drug addiction then I wouldn't have had the motivation to do most of my daily actions. In a sense, I was lucky that I found a motivation inside of me, albeit was for a negative reason but it gave me a reason to go to work and to keep my employment. The painful realisation is that; to be in our best position for mental health then all areas of our life need to be in order to some degree. The home we reside in, our connection to our loved ones, having a purpose or goal, finances and physical health all play an important factor. We can choose to feed our body with junk food and hope it doesn't fail its next MOT or we can eat healthy and cross our fingers that our effort is rewarded. We could extend this analogy to our mind, trash in and trash out. Another primary condition could be causing the depression which would imply; that tackling the source could alleviate the symptoms and eventually resolve the issue. Digging deep down inside yourself and discovering the root of your problems can help move things along quicker. I always knew what caused my depression, but I set myself up for failure and was also let down by the supporting services. The wait times were several months, and sometimes up to years to be seen for mental health conditions. I threw fuel into the fire by drinking alcohol in an attempt to sink my problems to the bottom of the ocean. However, if someone had intervened and offered some advice for coping with my trauma and imparted some coping mechanisms or techniques then I may have healed sooner. I guess we will never know......

An excellent tool I would like to share with you is a simple yet informative one; we will call this tool - *My Life List*. With a pen and paper you should find a quiet place that you feel comfortable with.

Title two sections; one heading for *Like,* and one heading for *Dislike.*

In each section start compiling a list for each category, one filled with all of the things that you do in your life that makes you happy and in the other section add things of the opposite effect. An example would be; walking my dog – which for me would go in the *Like* list. A boring task like washing my clothes – would be in the *Dislike* list for me. The second task is to add up your list of *Likes* verses *Dislikes* and analyse whether you can decrease any *Dislikes* or increase how often you do a task from your *Like* list. You do not have to be a genius to realise that if your *Dislike* list greatly outweighs the *Like* list then you are already living at a disadvantage. The final stage is to analyse the *Dislike* list further, planning any ideas or positive steps you could take to reduce or impact the dislike list. Obviously, we cannot pay less rent money to our landlord, but if we owe the landlord money which is causing us stress then a positive step could be to seek financial advice, or to offer them a repayment plan. If we have more negative tasks than positive, then why not increase how often you walk your dog, or visit a friend more often who brings you comfort and love? We will always have to do tasks that we do not enjoy doing, but the trick is to ensure that we have a healthy balance, if we become weighed down with negative tasks then we leave ourselves open to depression. The above task only works if you are honest and mature, because we can always affect a situation with how we respond to it. People are quick to build a business plan or a financial plan but we often neglect a much needed self-care plan. Humans often ignore the signs of poor mental health until it is too late. It is usually the dramatic act of a breakdown that causes people to take stock and cater for what truly matters. My advice is; do not wait for a mental breakdown, analyse yourself and advocate for your own wellbeing with the same ferocity that you would for an animal or child who was being mistreated. Be fierce, for you matter and the world is a better place with you in it.

As Frank used to say, it is good to talk. Be honest with your friends or loved ones, people can only support you if they are aware of what is going on inside of that head of yours. Reach out to someone and let them know that you need help; having a strong support-network can be life changing. I confided in close friends and I am glad that I did.

When I feel myself being out of balance I tell my partner immediately, and I am sure he is grateful for the warning. Steven can monitor my behaviour and adjust his responses accordingly. We all make leeway for a friend who is in pain or when they are not acting their usual self. I also take more walks in nature, I find being outside helps to clear my head and it aids me in feeling more grounded. Take your shoes off and walk on the grass, wiggle your toes and feel the earth beneath your feet. This is more pleasurable if the grass is dry rather than wet, but I live in the UK, so the rain visits often. Another trick that I find helps to sooth me is by indulging in a hot bath, this is not a regular treat for me as I live in a property on a water meter so I often avoid running excess water. I mentioned the advantages of reaching out to friends for support, but the place I seek the most help from is the spirit world. I ask my guides and deceased loved ones for help every chance that I get. I am sure somewhere on another plane is a Being of a higher vibration, rolling their metaphoric eyes while answering yet another one of my prayers. It may surprise you to know that when I do make a trip to visit my doctor they welcome my holistic approach, it is common for doctors to recommend reading, natural remedies and wellbeing treatments for conditions. Meditation and mindfulness plays an important factor for patients living with painful or long-term conditions. I have never had a doctor roll their eyes at me, or respond negatively when I share with them my holistic treatments or practices. This brings us back to the power of the mind and our attitude, with the fascinating effect it has on a patient's results and wellbeing. The placebo effect could be considered when we achieve a good outcome from our positive approach or spiritual practices. One could argue that it is all in my mind, and that the simple act of performing spiritual healing could be causing me to feel better similar to taking a placebo. I would like to explore this further, for example; what if instead of my mind and body being affected similar to a placebo that instead you consider the possibility that I healed myself with manifestation? By using visual techniques we can fantasise about a dream or goal that we desire, we can then use this technique to reach goals and meet targets. A non-believer may suggest that the same outcome is achieved by manifestation rather than to agree that a person has been receiving healing from the spiritual world. Let's travel further down the rabbit hole, another option is to assume that the person has healed or alleviated their pain due to medical science. Once I meditate and open myself up for healing, I believe that I will receive help, therefore my mind calms, my body responds by reducing my blood pressure and therefore, I do end up feeling better or in less pain. These are all valuable theories, but the interesting part is that the results are still the same both ways; and the person seeking help or healing is left feeling slightly better than they did before. Therefore it works, whether you believe that the healing is coming from the spirit world, the universal energy or from a placebo effect.

There are many ways to seek help if you are feeling depressed, with the most common option being to make contact with your doctor.

*"Into the dark I fall each day, into the hole where there is no day. How far I fall I have no say, come find me lord for I've lost my way." – Bryony Best*

## Chapter 11

## (Guest Chapter)

## S. Best

# Multiple Sclerosis

I have always led a very active life. Training in Martial Arts since a very young age, it became my passion, my life, my identity. I had a very successful competitive career, winning regional, national, and international tournaments. I was always driven to be unbeatable, no matter whom my opponent was. This resolve would be tested throughout my life.

Aged 13, I had a 2.5 tonne lorry engine crush my right foot, initially I was told that I may never walk properly again, let alone compete, within 2 years I won my first regional tournament.

Aged 27, my right ankle was shattered, requiring pins and a steel plate to be fitted. I was told I'd never be able to train again. I had my first cage fight 6 months later.

Aged 34, I was in a car crash, fracturing 2 of my vertebrae, again Doctors seemed doubtful I'd walk or be mobile. A few weeks later I was back to work as a Doorman at a local nightclub.

So, at the age of 43 I was away on week 8 of a 10-week training course for a new career as a prison officer, when I woke up one morning completely blind in my right eye with only about 20% vision in my left eye. I was immediately sent to the local hospital for testing. After hours of tests and scans I was informed that I had Optic Neuritis, which can be an early indication of Multiple Sclerosis. A week later that diagnosis was confirmed. I sat in the consultation room being told yet again, that I would have to alter my lifestyle, even to the point that I was told to re-think my new career choice as in their professional opinion; I would be unable to carry out the duties of a prisoner officer with my new diagnosis. I must admit that I knew very little about MS (Multiple Sclerosis), so I asked the consultant what effect it would have on me. His first response was to tell me that it would shorten my life by at least 10 years straight away, and that I would probably be in a wheelchair sooner rather than later.

I left the hospital with a sense of dread, replaying in my mind all the information 'Dr Doom and Gloom' had delivered me. The rest of the day was a very sombre one, and I felt overwhelmed with negative thoughts. The next stage was denial, surely, they must have been wrong, after all, these experts had repeatedly told me I wouldn't walk, or wouldn't compete, and I had proved them wrong time and time again. Then acceptance came, followed by research. I tried to learn as much as I could about MS, and what I could do to fight it. I met with specialist consultants, discussed treatments and I received more information to get a better informed opinion of what I should expect from my condition. I also set in place a support network with the MS Society, my family, and my friends. My MS consultant informed me that I met the criteria for a fairly new type of treatment called Ocrelizumab (Ocrevus), which is an infusion used in the treatment of Relapsing Remitting MS which I was diagnosed with. I had my initial 2 infusions a few weeks apart, then every 6 months I have an 8hr infusion. For me, this seemed like the least intrusive treatment as it only took up 1 day of my life every 6 months.

For those readers, who like me initially, know very little about Multiple Sclerosis I will try and give you a brief crash course. Multiple Sclerosis is currently an incurable disease, where the body's nervous system attacks itself. This is why I initially lost my vision, as my own immune system was attacking my optic nerves. It can also cause spasms in the nerves throughout the body, for me it's primarily in my legs. This was an issue that I had prior to my diagnosis, but it was dismissed by Doctors as symptoms caused by my broken back from my car crash years earlier. Another main attribute of MS is fatigue. Now, I don't mean feeling slightly tired, this is an all-consuming complete lack of energy which can strike at any time and without warning. It can leave you without the energy to walk, or to even lift your arms up, making normal functions like getting dressed, washing, or even eating, the hardest of chores.

I had an incident once, when I was walking down my stairs and my legs just stopped responding. This was apparently due to the signals from my brain not relaying the messages to my legs, so in my mind I was still walking down the stairs, but the reality was that my legs just stopped working. I took a nasty fall down the stairs, and this was a real eye-opener into some of the effects of my condition.

Through my research I learnt that stress and lack of rest and sleep can exasperate the symptoms and accelerate the condition. This was just what I didn't need to hear, as I had just joined one of the top 5 most stressful jobs in the country, and I have suffered with insomnia for most of my life, only sleeping up to 4 hours a night on average! I quickly realised that this disease wasn't simply going to go away, and I now literally had the fight of my life on my hands.

One of the first things to change was my diet. Through my research I started taking Vitamin D daily, as a lack of this can contribute to MS. Some studies suggest that for people who already have MS, vitamin D may offer some benefits. These benefits include lessening the frequency and severity of their symptoms, improving quality of life, and lengthening the time it takes to progress from relapsing-remitting multiple sclerosis to the secondary-progressive phase. Eating lots of greens and vegetables became a steady addition to my meals. My partner also regularly made sure I ate plenty of peppers, kidney beans, and I also started eating pistachio nuts in the evenings. We started using thyme to season most of my meals as this also has proven results in slowing down the effects of MS, and I also take turmeric capsules. I kept a positive mindset throughout the early stages of my diagnosis, vowing that I would continue as normal for as long as I could. For a brief time, I took CBD oil as this was meant to be greatly beneficial for people with MS, however, for me the benefits were minimal, but the expense wasn't.

My partner and I started jogging regularly together, and I continued to train and teach Martial Arts and despite initially being told I wouldn't be able to continue training, I graded last year attaining my 4th degree black belt (4 years after my diagnosis). I have now lived with this condition for a number of years and against everything I was told by the experts, I still work for the prison service. Not only am I still operational within the service, but I am the C&R co-ordinator (control and restraint) for the largest and most violent prison in the UK. I am also a C&R instructor, and advanced trained/Tornado (which is like the riot squad in the police).

I'm very aware that I could easily wake up tomorrow blind, or unable to walk, but until that happens, I will continue to live my life as I want, and not as someone else tells me to live it. It is this mindset and attitude which I think has helped me through the last 5 years. It would be very easy for me to give in and just stay in bed, rather than get up at 03:30 every morning and drive 70 miles to London to work. By forcing myself every day to get up and get out, I have managed to stay productive in society, to the point where most people I meet find it hard to comprehend that I have such a debilitating disability. I keep focused, keep busy, stay fit, and this strongly contributes to my overall well-being. Alongside the conventional approach to managing my condition, I have regular Reiki sessions with my partner who is a Reiki master. I also have reflexology when I can afford it. We have our own gym in our garage, and I stretch regularly to help combat the pain and discomfort I feel most days. As corny as this next part will sound, my greatest solace has been love.

The love I receive constantly from those around me. The intense love I have for my partner and my family helps keep me focused on the important things in life. My daughter and my fiancé keep me strong, making me feel like I must keep fighting every day, so I don't let them down. The newest addition to our family is our

Chihuahua. Fully grown at 2.2kg, she brings me such joy and happiness. Her unconditional love, which only comes from a devoted pet, raises my spirits, and gives me another reason to live life to the fullest. We are inseparable (except when going to work), and she travels everywhere with us. She is our 'Fur baby' and being around her helps keep me relaxed, easing the pressures and stress of my life.

At the time of writing this my condition is still stable, without any major flare-ups. I still have my infusions every 6 months, I have a yearly MRI scan, and regular appointments with my MS specialist and the MS nursing team.

I've spent 5 years now living with this disease, going to bed every night not knowing if I will wake up blind or crippled, but I push this negativity to the back of my mind and focus on life one day at a time. I take stock of what I can do and strive to do more.

I still love martial arts and train as much as I can. I may not train at the same level or with the same intensity I once had, and my techniques might not be as crisp or as fast as they once were, but I'm still doing it! That gives me pride, and focus.

The best advice I can give to anyone in a similar position is:

*"Don't worry about the things you can't do, just do what you can, when you can. Listen to your body, know your limits, and ignore both. Push yourself, especially when all seems lost or hopeless. Most importantly, never give up and never stop fighting!"*

*- S. Best*

# Chapter 12

## (Guest Chapter)

### Gemma

# Fibromyalgia

My name is Gemma and I am married with three beautiful children; Lilly 10 years of age, Poppy who is 15 years old and my eldest son George who is 17. In 2020, I returned to live in Hampshire after living in Plymouth for several years due to my husband's Naval job. I am an average person who has experienced a few bumps in the road, one of them bumps being my health, as I have always had issues medically. I work at a local care home part-time and I care for my busy house-hold plus many pets. I am obsessed with my guinea pigs and dogs, I take the dogs for walks daily and I have an inside home built for my guinea pigs that sits with pride inside my living room. I met my husband George when we were just little kids, I was 6 years old, and it was years later and after my first failed marriage that led me to be reunited with him in 2011. I am a proud mama who dotes on her children and I love bragging about their endless talents. I like to think of myself as a strong person, I have been through some difficult shit in my life and yet I am still here to tell the tale. My daily routine consists of getting the children off to school, feeding my pets and adding fresh water to their bowls before I leave my house to walk to work. I do not drive as I have a decease called Retinitus Pigmonosa, also known as RP. RP is a genetic disease meaning that I was born with it, thinking back to my childhood I had displayed symptoms early on but everyone assumed that I was just clumsy. The disease slowly makes cells in the retina break down which causes vision loss, and unfortunately there is no cure for it. My mum was diagnosed with it many years ago and I supported her, we both felt the fear, followed by relief and dread. The final stage is to accept the diagnosis and then to move forward to make memories while you still have some vision. Eventually, my father had to quit his job and care for my mum full-time, I helped out when I could before I moved away to Plymouth in 2013. It was the move to Plymouth that motivated me to learn to drive so I could make the 200 mile journey to visit my family back in Portsmouth. While living in Plymouth, I started getting intense migraines and my driving instructor noticed that I missed some obvious obstructions like cars changing lanes and traffic light changes. Concerns for my symptoms are what pushed me to eventually seek medical help which is what led to my diagnosis. Anyway, this is why I do not drive and why I have to walk to work as there are no obvious bus routes for me to use either. My walks to my employment were becoming increasingly unbearable, I started to feel like I was ill or coming down with the flu, my body ached all over and my daily routine was becoming unbearable. My job requires me to be on the go for several hours a day, working for an activity department in a large care home.

Have you ever woken up in the morning and felt that heavy aching feeling, and thought to yourself..... oh no..... I've caught a virus or something? That's what happened one morning in November 2021. My morning started with me feeling completely wiped out, with my body aching from head to toe and with a heavy fog in my brain similar to when you've had a hangover, only without the fun night out before. Of course being the type of person I am, I popped some pain pills, sunk a couple of strong coffees and went about my day. Oh, if only I knew that day what lay ahead for me!

A few weeks had passed and I seemed to only get worse and now to add to my problems I wasn't sleeping, waking in the night with searing pain running from my lower spine through to my hips, knees and into my feet, as what I can only describe as electric shocks that just kept coming thick and fast. I remember going into my place of work on a Sunday with the most peculiar feeling, and that's when it all really began. People were talking to me, I could see their lips moving but the sound wasn't there. I was moving at a snail's pace, like dragging my legs through mud and yet the environment around me was moving so fast that I couldn't catch my breath. This was my first experience of vertigo, yet another symptom had crept in, what was happening? On the Monday morning I contacted my GP surgery, we were coming out of Covid restrictions at this time but the NHS was still under so much pressure. I was desperate to be seen by my doctor but it was not possible, I tried my hardest and I pushed through the pain and symptoms. I was struggling at home and I found it all too overwhelming, I kept my true pain levels and fear from my work colleagues too. I even took on more responsibilities at work when my boss was involved in a serious car crash in December, so with no choice, I continued to muddle through until the New Year.

Christmas came and went, the decorations were taken down and everyone returned to work and school. I had booked some well deserved time off and was looking forward to having the house to myself, plus my GP had finally got back in contact with me and finally ordered some tests. My week of annual leave began well, I planned to see friends and to get some boring adult bits done around the house. Mid-week I woke up at 6am as always, got ready and set off on my dog walk by 7.30am. As I plodded along with my Jack Russell named Jethro the world began to spin, faster and faster; here we go again, only this time my vision was fading (I was used to this with my RP condition but not usually mixed with vertigo, nausea and now boom...the electric shocks!) My world had spun upside down and all within 60 seconds. I had to concentrate so hard on getting myself home safely; I was petrified that I wouldn't make it. Looking as white as a sheet I walked through the front door and collapsed into a chair.

The look of worry on my husband's face was terrifying.

I've been through a lot in my life, even the happier parts of it somehow were shrouded in grief or trauma, but I always found my way through it, mentally and physically. I look back at when this all began and think to myself "why oh why didn't you listen to your body?" You see as time passed, and by time, I mean the 17 weeks it took me to see a GP and the further 12 months it took me to be diagnosed, I was disappearing down the rabbit hole, and tiny little parts of me had started to fade away. I didn't leave the house unless it was to go to work or to collect my children. Every time I had to socialise with others, I would take a deep breath and say "keep smiling, just 6 hours more until you're finished" or "just nod in the right places until we get home", It even got to the point that I was physically terrified of leaving the house. I would sob quietly to myself and then try to calm my fear. I told my husband how I didn't want to wake up in the morning, I would cry out in the middle of the night in horrific pain, often sleeping for no more than 45 minutes at a time. I had no patience for the ones I love or those who I cared for. All of this pain and disruption because of Fibromyalgia, and my mind was constantly living with the fear of overdoing it or pushing myself too far which could then send me into a fibro-flare. I was forced to change my whole life, from my duties at home to my employment too. I was strung out on pain medication and my pill box was way too large for a person of my age. My boss reassessed my employer risk assessment; they had previously made arrangements for me to receive lifts to and from work when working through the darker evenings. The original risk assessment was in place due to my RP, but now I had a new medical condition to be considered. At first, I was asked to not deliver exercise classes or to carry out any manual handling which helped me out, we also reduced my hours, and I was taken off of working weekends too. This was all great and I felt supported, but it was no use, I was still struggling with my other duties and the shift hours. I was either in too much pain or I was strung out high on pain medication. Thank the heavens for my parents, husband and children. They all supported me as much as they could but I felt like shit. I had no life; it was ripped away from me by this vile disease. I started eating junk food and my once small frame started to slowly grow. I could hardly walk let alone exercise, but I did get small moments of joy from my children and pets. Eventually, I was invited to join a spiritual development group for beginners with one of my good friends. I had always been interested in spiritualism, but I was also scared too, as I had experienced dark things in my past. In the group we were taught how to work with energy, how to meditate and ask for healing. It was amazing. I was learning how to harness a power greater than I had ever felt before and I could put it to good use too. I found myself mediating and paying more attention to my own energy and body. We also experimented with crystals, tarot cards and clairvoyance. I attended my friends cabin every Thursday evening for 10 weeks or so, we had to be careful due to covid so we took tests before gathering, plus I worked with her too so we were used to taking precautions. One thing we learnt was how to use a crystal pendulum to assess our chakras, plus the practical way to feel energy with the palms of our hands. It was empowering to have access to this knowledge and I now had a tool box at my disposal, the healing wasn't a cure as the techniques were simply holistic tools to aid me while living with my medical conditions. It was sad when the course ended but my friend had recorded a guided meditation for us all to use when we were at home, and I will never forget what I have learnt from her.

As the next few months passed by, I entered a new phase of my condition and I felt a sudden urge to take control, but a medical condition like this is not something you can easily handle let alone control. I had been going through teeth correction and it was finally coming towards the end, I was only allowed to eat white coloured food. This new diet for my teeth motivated me to eat healthy and to lose some weight, but something was stopping me and they were little round pills. I slowly started a plan to reduce my pain medication, safely taking on more physical activity while I observed my body and pain levels. I went into my new experiment with an open mind, but was also preparing myself for possible failure and pain. I was pleasantly surprised when a few weeks had passed and I started to notice a difference, I am still in the middle of this new life style but I feel positive so far. I try and meditate when I can and ask the spirit world for healing, alongside using my pain medication but not at the same high level as I was previously. My friend informed me that she had noticed a great difference in me, yet the only true change was my mindset. At first I was angry and felt defeated and I still get days when I feel this way. The next phase was when I felt acceptance of my new condition and restrictions, acceptance didn't cure me, but it did help me to take more notice of what I could and couldn't do. My current phase is like a wave of motivation, that sometimes falls beneath the surface causing me to fall into darkness; the trick is to not stay in the darkness. I have plans, places that I want to go and milestones that I want to experience with my children and husband. I may fall down to the ground but I will continue to get back up again, for my family and for me. My advice would be to try and find what works for you, for me it is the simple things like taking a hot bath with salts followed by a tens pain relief machine and an acupuncture mat. I also use a pregnancy pillow in bed, follow a strict sleep schedule and I take time for me. I prune my eyebrows, paint my nails and focus on loving myself.

My husband has this saying, "you can only piss with the cock you've got". He is so right, as I wasted so much time and energy trying to fight the fibromyalgia when what I really needed to do was to accept it. I have learnt how to slow down, listen to my body and allow others to take over. It is okay to say "I need help", and to listen to my body when it tells me it has had enough for now. The ironic thing about people living with a pain condition, is that many of them use the *Spoon Theory*; you wake up with X number of spoons and each task requires the use of one of them. I had a tattoo of a spoon on my chest in 2015, my husband has a big spoon and I have a smaller spoon, but now the tattoo has two meanings. Our lives were entwined since childhood and yet who would have thought that in 2011 our paths would cross again, leading to a whirlwind relationship followed by our marriage in 2013. I am loved and admired everyday by the most wonderful man I know; my husband.

He reassures me often saying, "you are doing okay Gem, keep going!"

# Chapter 13

## (Guest Chapter)

## Brand

# Cancer

My name is Brand and my whole life has been dedicated to fitness and eating healthy. I did dabble in alcohol and drugs when I was a teenager, maybe from the age of fifteen until my early twenties. I tried to smoke but it didn't work for me, I remember attempting to smoke in the shadows at a park one evening and I had lit the wrong end of a cigarette, and it caused the other kids to fall into a fit of laughter. That experience put me off of smoking for life. I did partake in casual drinking with my group of primary school friends. We would scratch some money together and use our few pounds to buy some beers or a 3 litre bottle of Ace Cider. I know this sounds unhealthy from the start but to me it was normal and something all children tried and experimented with at that age. Eventually I moved away from my friends who were living in Portchester, with a big push from my mum I managed to find a studio flat that looked like a white castle, near to Elm Grove and Albert Road in Portsmouth. My mother had shocked me with news that she would soon be moving away to Greece, and I was given a few weeks to find a new place to live. I was working as a supervisor at Natures Way in Chichester, when I first moved out of my parental home. The studio flat was small and had one waist high wall which separated the bedroom, kitchen and the lounge area. It was not good, having to share a toilet and shower with ten other occupants, most of who were female. I felt excited when I moved into my studio flat, I was given a new responsibility to select and choose my own cleaning products. I thought I was living in the music capital of the world due to the high number of live music venues and instrument shops in my local area. Two venues from the area that have closed down since the year - 2000 are; the Horseshoe and the Priory. I also liked to walk around Steve's Drum-Pad and the Boom Room, I enjoyed eyeing up their drum kits and imagining how it would feel when I would one day buy a kit for myself to use. My dad was a musician, so I had been exposed to music and his guitar from an early age. I can recall the moment that I decided I wanted to learn how to play an instrument; I was nine years of age sat with my friends while watching a VHS tape of Guns N Roses (Live in Tokyo). The drummer Matt Sorum played a drum solo, and I had never heard drums being played like that before. As a group of teenage boys we all decided that we would form a band and each learn a different instrument. After a week had passed I had managed to buy a drum kit for £150 from Steve's Drum-Pad shop, and I had started to learn the drums all by myself - with YouTube not having been invented yet. My friends within that week had made a pact but given up, so our band broke up before we had even begun. It was great for me to have music to focus on, as I was a very angry and violent child; I was suspended from school frequently for getting into fights with other pupils. My motto was to hit first, no questions asked. I continued with my music and a few years later in secondary school, I formed a band with other musicians who were of a similar age to me. Our band was called Etikut and we played mainly indie-rock music, we even played at venues including the Air Balloon in Portsmouth, and the Horseshoe pub. Our lead singer managed to convince his mum to buy our band a PA system and to hire a studio to record our own music; we recorded three songs onto our demo disc. I still have my own copy and it felt amazing to be in a studio, it felt like I was born to be a musician. I planned out a route to help me become a rock star, this involved recording three band albums and then I would go solo when I reached stardom. I believed this dream would be achieved, and this feeling was amplified when my brother Arren's friends had given him positive feedback after listening to my demo disc. Music was a big part of my life and has been a positive passion and focus for me, from playing live music to attending festivals and gigs. It felt like the bar was officially open when I turned eighteen and started living in Portsmouth, I frequented bars and clubs, meeting interesting people and making new friends. I was never a big drinker and I managed to avoid becoming an alcoholic or drug taker as my body and brain wouldn't let me. I am a controlling person and the idea of letting go and giving into the addictions was too much for me, even though I desired a rock star lifestyle, similar to Guns N Roses, Aerosmith and Motley Crew. A few years later when I was entering my twenties, I felt the social pressure of body image. I overheard a work colleague refer to me as the tall, skinny supervisor and that description stayed with me. An interest was sparked, and I wanted to change my body and to become more of a man. The first step I took was to purchase some cheap, shitty, weights from Argos, plus two cheap tubs of weight gain powder. The weights were plastic coated and filled with clay which overtime resulted in the clay cracking and dislodging, making me feel like I was carrying two big, baby rattles instead of weights. I started eating full fat food and extra large portions to add some weight to my slim 6ft frame. It only took three months until I started to notice my body changing; this then motivated me to join Ed's Gym in Albert Road, Portsmouth. I attended his gym four to five days a week, from the age of twenty until I was thirty three years of age. I still went to a few pubs and live gigs but with my new work out regime, I hardly drank any alcohol, and I never became a smoker. I worked many different jobs over the years in the security industry including Gunwarf Quays, Crown Courts, Portsmouth University, and many local clubs. Between working multiple jobs covering up to 90 hours a week, I always managed to find time to train at the gym even if it required a 3am pump. I lived with my sister Bryony at various addresses in Portsmouth until we were evicted from our current home due to its sale in June 2015. That move was a very stressful time for me, but to explain it properly I will have to take you back to 2013.

I remember waking up one morning with a severe pain in my stomach, as I became more alert, I realised the pain was coming from my bollocks. It felt like I had been kicked in the balls, and I couldn't move. Confusion came over me and I didn't know what to do! In a state of panic I telephoned my girlfriend, I informed her of my symptoms and said that I couldn't move. I was taken to QA (Queen Alexandra) hospital and I waited to be assessed in their Accident and Emergency department. My mind was racing but I had no idea what was wrong with me, I had an army doctor and five more separate doctors who checked over me. They all came to the same diagnosis; that I must have slept funny on it. On the car ride home, neither of us agreed with their assessment but they were the experts so what could we do? After leaving the hospital, I went straight to my employment of work despite my painful condition as I was between night shifts. For two days the symptoms slowly improved until they disappeared completely.

One year later in 2014, I woke up in bed with the same pain as I had in 2013, and we were soon due to fly to Los Angeles for a holiday of a lifetime. I tried to ignore my pain but my partner wouldn't let me, she forced me to call my doctor to get an emergency appointment. My GP checked me over and telephoned the hospital in front of me to demand that they scan my testicles immediately. As we drove towards the hospital I was more concerned with my upcoming holiday that my partner and I had saved many years to pay for. I was sent to various departments, and every room that I walked into had posters for cancer on the walls with leaflets in trays. Looking around in each waiting room, I noticed patients wearing bandanas on their heads, and many sickly-looking people. After my scan I was called into an ultrasound appointment before being left in a waiting area. I was alone when I had my scans and tests, my girlfriend was not allowed to accompany me inside. I made my way towards Rachel to tell her how embarrassing my scans were, when I noticed the nurse who had just scanned me, running down the corridor with paperwork clenched in her fist. After a short wait I was invited into a small room with a doctor who handed me a leaflet and informed me that they had found a lump and it was likely cancerous and she had booked my surgery for two days later plus a follow up appointment for after the operation. My first thought was concern for telling my partner that our holiday of a lifetime would have to be put on hold, as my surgery had been booked for the same day as our flight! I waved at my girlfriend to follow me and we made it to the stairwell before I finally broke the news, and I just fell to the ground. My body was overflowing with emotion and my body just slumped to the floor, I was only thirty two years of age. Rachel couldn't believe her ears and she started to weep...............

The next thing I recall is standing outside the hospital and bumping into my sister, she had been crying and looked distressed. As we slowly walked towards the car park I felt my legs start to speed up, I needed to reach the car before I shared my news with Bryony. As we approached Rachel's vehicle, Bryony showed me her surgery forms, she had been booked for an ectopic pregnancy evacuation for the same date as my surgery! I repeated my news to my sister, and she stood stunned in silence. I quickly moved on to plan my day and evening, deciding whether to break the news to my family or employer first. We visited my employer, and then I went to the gym followed by breaking the news to my mum and my two brothers. My mum took the news the hardest, crying out hysterically to the heavens above, "not my Brand, don't you take my Brand from me".

I had the surgery at QA hospital and learnt that I had Teratoma cancer, which is 98% aggressive. I ignored the recovery period and I returned to work a few days later with a walking stick. All seemed fine and my monthly tests were negative for the following year until June, 2015. My sister had also frequently given me spiritual healing from her group of trainees who were learning spiritual development with her.

In June, 2015 I was sat in the control room at work which was based in central Portsmouth, when I received a phone call from the hospital. On the telephone call I was informed that my test results indicate that the cancer had returned, my blood markers were raised and they found abnormalities in my CT scan. It looked like the cancer could be in my stomach, spine and kidney but they were not certain. I was left with the life changing news, and a torturous several days before my next appointment was booked to discuss it further. I attended the appointment with my sister and partner, it was then explained that they wanted to pump me with their highest intensity of chemotherapy. I was booked for ten hours a day, for four days a week at Southampton General hospital, but they felt positive that the treatment would cure me. I was shocked that it had returned, even more so than I had been with my first diagnosis of cancer. The chemo was horrific, as I sat in a room with many other patients who were at different stages of their cancer journey. The smell was horrendous, it was like sanitizer, but a dying patient gave me some great advice, to take my anti-sickness tablets every three hours. To my left side was a French man named Jacques, he started his treatment on the same date as me, but his body couldn't take it anymore and he sadly died. I was very angry with my cancer, I felt other people deserved it more than I did, I didn't even smoke or drink. Obviously one of the two cigarettes that I smoked as a teenager must have had cancer in it (joking). Over the next few months, I managed to watch myself turn into a zombie, grey skin with sunken eyes, hair loss and I also had the shits, a symptom from Chemotherapy. I was either constantly on the toilet or I was hugging it. I vomited, which was expected but the real surprise was when I was admitted to hospital with back spasms and extreme pain. It was caused from my doctor misdiagnosing me and prescribing stomach injections, usually prescribed to help produce more blood cells but I didn't even need them. My sister and her partner rushed me to hospital, and it was apparent that they couldn't help as my veins had collapsed, and I needed morphine. I was sent home with no pain relief and my sister was forced to acquire Oramorph through unofficial channels. I kept pushing through the chemo as I believed that it would help me, I also contacted local businesses who donated food supplements, to help me maintain my weight throughout my treatment. I still exercised at home with my weights but towards the end, I couldn't really manage to complete any training. I sadly lost my hearing in my left ear which affected my balance and ability to play my musical instruments. By now, I had acquired a grand piano, many guitars and a harmonica. By the end of my treatment, I was excited to be invited for a consultation; I was holding my breath while I waited for the doctor to say those magical words.... The cancer is all gone.

They are not the words that I heard, instead the doctor said to me "the chemo has worked to reduce the size of your tumours, but we have now discovered that you have a second type of cancer that is unresponsive to chemotherapy. We will now need to perform surgery to remove many lymph nodes and maybe your kidney".

I was booked for major surgery, the doctors planned on cutting me from sternum to navel. They would remove my organs from my chest and reach through to remove the tumour in my back, as they feared any other option could be fatal or cause me to be paralysed. They had no idea whether I would lose a kidney or if I would even be able to walk again.

The day of my surgery was horrific; I was dreading the possibility of being paralysed from the waist down. Shortly after waking from surgery, I was informed that the doctor had removed the tumour along with fourteen lymph nodes.

I started to feel immense pain after my surgery; I had six tubes and cables coming out of my body, three in my stomach, two in my arm and one in my dick! I also felt a wave of happiness and relief, as I could move my feet, which was great as it meant I wasn't paralysed from the surgery. I spent five days in hospital recovering, which was made worse by the fact the hospital was short of space, so they had to put dementia patients in my ward with recovering surgery patients. I had not slept at all as I had to endure continuous screaming and moaning all day and night, I was so happy and relieved when I finally left the hospital to return home. I was so determined to get my fitness levels back to normal, I started using hand-springs to squeeze at first, then I moved onto doing three laps of the coffee table before eventually pigeon stepping up the stairs. The next few months were filled with highs and lows, my body was different and I wasn't able to do what I wanted to do. My partner cared for me, making my meals and encouraging me to keep progressing. It can be emotionally draining and physically exhausting to fight cancer, the process is made more stressful when you add in the financial impact the disease has on your life. My sister continued to give me spiritual healing and I stayed motivated to get my life and health back into order. I added natural cancer fighting foods to my diet like blueberries, and I take Ceylon Cinnamon, Omega 3 pill, Multivitamins, Vitamin C, Osteocare Vitamin D, Maringa Plant Powder, and 100% pure Multivitamin Fruit Juice. Always consult your GP before taking any supplements or natural remedies, as it is always best to consult an expert.

Fast forward to February 2017, which is when I noticed I had been struggling with bright light and I had a slight swelling of my right eye. I booked an appointment with the eye specialist at the hospital. They checked my eye and told me I had a growth on my right eye and that it needed to be removed, as soon as they checked my hospital records, alarm bells rang because I had a history with cancer, so the surgery was rushed through. Now, having open eye surgery whilst awake was the most horrific thing I think I've ever experienced, not being able to look away as someone comes at your eye with a scalpel and scissors is not the most comfortable feeling. They removed the growth and I was glad to be informed that it wasn't cancerous. I was now thirty five years of age and had already experienced three surgeries relating to cancer.

2023 - I have now been cancer free for over five years, I believe the main three factors that got me through cancer were; firstly my fitness and training, secondly my strong character and fuck you attitude. And thirdly and most importantly is my wife, Rachel, who was with me and by my side every step of the way. Without her unwavering love and support I would never have kicked cancers ass! I still live in fear of the cancer returning every day of my life but I am happy, I know that whatever life throws at me I can beat it and overcome it. I have always used humour to tackle my real difficult situations in life, since day one I've been trying to put whatever kind of funny, positive spin I can on my cancer journey.

*"Cancer is just a chapter in our lives and is not the whole story."* – Allie Moreno

*"Cancer is a part of our life, but it is not our whole life."* - Nick Prochak

*"Giving in to the darkness offers no benefit."*- Marivel Preciado

# Chapter 14

# Life

I am writing this book as a thirty nine year old female, I have previously been traumatized, lost and left in the darkness to rot.

But I have never been bested.

I have been beaten up, left battered and bruised with cuts that sting and lumps that were too sore to touch. I have stomped through my concrete city in search of hope while wearing a cloak of sadness, but yet I am still here. After subjecting my body and mind to absurd amounts of alcohol and drugs, I suffered a psychotic break. I never gave up, even though I wanted to. Sliding down a hard wooden door, I have cried out in pain, sobbing in grief and despair. Yet I still love and am loved. I use to question my sanity on a daily basis, wondering if Brand or my family truly did exist. I would reach out to feel the material of a table against my skin or the fabric of a chair in an attempt to grasp some tiny fragment of reality. My mind was broken, shattered into a million atoms, yet I am still here.

All I have ever known is pain, physical and psychological. With my axe made of steel, I dug deep into my soul, cutting out the pain and losing fragments of myself with it. I became my own hero. Slayer of demons and heroine to the lost and lonely souls is my new name. Humans are divine and stronger than they will ever know. We embody a strength that even mighty powerful dragons and wizards would envy. For every drop of darkness that falls from the sky, a larger and brighter light will fall. You just have to open your eyes and heart to all the wonders and energy around you. It is easy to become blind when walking through the darkness, similar to how we can instantly fall deaf, missing cries for help from our loved ones. I am a hyper focused person and this is both my magic power and my kryptonite. I live a busy lifestyle at present, but I have a plan to reduce my commitments to find a better balance within my life. The plan is to quit my main employment and to concentrate solely on my writing and spiritualism. I am often asked how I manage to keep up with my marketing, home life, jobs, socialising and wellbeing. My answer is that I have temporarily sacrificed my social life; I have reduced my sleeping hours and increased my working hours. I use my tool box of holistic techniques to aid my gruelling regime but they are not a cure. I am fully aware that no human can burn the candle at both ends, even if both ends consist of only work and no play. I am currently being naughty and ignoring my body, hoping it will at least get me to the next gas station.

What techniques do I find the most effective?

Being in nature and soaking up its energy makes me feel rejuvenated. Staring into the trees and feeling the breeze brush gently against my skin gives my body strength and joy, as does the warm heat of sun on my face. Snuggling with my dog fills my heart with so much love, that it overflows and pours out of me. I highly recommend pet therapy for harbouring love in one's life. Spiritual healing helps me to top up my cup of energy, giving me what I need to keep on going. They say the best therapy is to have a chat with your friend, I haven't seen mine for a while but it is good to talk. I feel lighter after I have shared my worries and concerns, every time I catch up with Mercedes, it's like we could talk for days. And I always walk away with new motivation and a spring in my step. It is important to reach out, speak with your friends or loved ones; maybe you should consider joining a local support group.

Reading is the quickest way to slow down time, and to give your mind a much needed break from your own reality. I dream about reading, sitting with a steaming hot cup of tea, slouched on a beanbag chair at the foot of my back garden is heavenly. Find a hobby or a way to turn off your brain and focus on something more carefree and easy. Crystals are fabulous and pretty too, but they are also tiny little magic lumps ready to aid your healing journey. They resonate at different frequencies, affecting your own natural energy flowing through your chakras. They use quartz in HD TVs, watches, alarms, radios and many other technologies. Crystals can help to remove blockages and restore balance within your energy flow. It is important that you cleanse and recharge your crystals, but this act itself can be very spiritual. You can harness the earth, moon or sun to recharge them, or utilize sage, sea water, earth, moonlight, and visualization to cleanse them. I am also a fan of healing frequencies which is why I use a singing bowl; it impresses me to know that the Egyptians not only built their pyramids on the meridians of the earth, but that many have chambers built with healing frequencies inside. I find it a powerful experience to use Reiki dance and movement healing, with a similar effect achieved from drum therapy. There is a natural flow to the universe, imagine a sea of whirl pools and currents all clashing together and affecting one another. It can feel overwhelming to be in a public place, like a shopping centre, surrounded by hundreds of energies bombarding you simultaneously. If you could see other people's energies, you may be more selective to whom you expose yourself to. Obviously I am fussy which foods I put into my mouth, I have no choice in that matter but it is true that we need to feed our body and minds with a nutritional balance. You are what you eat and the company that you keep. There are many natural oils, foods and plants that can aid your healing or boost your immune system. I have tried ingesting safe oils and plants, I enjoyed using oils on my aura and I still spruce my energy with pure orange extracts. I grow herbs and use them within my menus, considering my conditions and my partners too. I do not have much time to allocate, but the time that I do have, I spend wisely. I may use up many hours of my day working and doing marketing or attending events and appointments, but that is what will help me to achieve my goals. I ask the spirit world and my guides for healing; I usually do this daily at present. You can access healing by simply asking the powers above for healing, or approaching your local spiritual church or a spiritual healer. Holistic therapies are everywhere, be sure to research and find out which ones may benefit you the most. I first learnt how to channel healing energy by attending a development group at Portsmouth Temple for Spiritualism. As the year went by, I took part in workshops run by local mediums and experts. My knowledge for reiki and crystals strengthened when I studied, I passed my diploma for crystal healing and I attuned to level 1 reiki, followed by level 2 and now I am a Reiki Master. Exercise is another great way to keep your body and mind in shape, obviously we get a nice reward of endorphins after we have endured a workout but physically, it can be life changing to keep you fit and active. Always speak with your doctor first and discuss any physical or holistic practices, to ensure they are safe and beneficial to your body and mind. Be present and not just a passenger on your own healing journey, so many people let others take control and they fail to contribute to their own goals and desires. Holistic approaches are a great addition to the primary medication and therapies that one may be prescribed. Personally, I vow that I am only able to cope with my experiences and illnesses due to my additional treatments, it is the whole approach and not the segment that completes it. The -*mind, body, =and spirit..*

Manifestation once scared me into submission; it also paralysed me rendering me still. I would wish for an umbrella and one would appear. Like the craft, I wanted silence, and I was deaf for days. The moment I realised that visualisation and manifestation was in the palm of my hand, I froze. What is the point in living my life if I could instantly get what I wanted? You may think that this sounds magnificent, but for me it made the game of life all too easy.

I hope you have found comfort, support or motivation from this book. These pages are filled with my truths and a few from my guest chapters too. I am sorry that I do not have a simpler answer for you, a one stop shop for all your medical needs. A magic pill that will take away all of your pain and suffering, that would be nice but I do not have one.

I do have the copious amounts of tried and tested tools that have worked for me, and hopefully you have been enlightened along the way.

You have all the tools you need inside of you, manifest your own surroundings and future in this existence. You paint your own canvass, so ensure that it is a work of art.

*"It is not the fear of failing, but the sober knowledge that you may have to fail before you can succeed." – Bryony Best*

*"Your positive action combined with positive thinking results in success." – Shiv Khera*

*"We are light, we are one, step into your power and shine." – Bryony Best*

# Final Message to the Reader

I would like to thank you from the bottom of my heart for purchasing and reading this book. Please do consider reading my other publications.

I do ask, that you please take the time to leave a review on the site where you purchased this book and do also add your review to Goodreads - if you have an account with them.

Please upload a picture with your review to your social media platforms as this will help others to find my book.

Website – www.bryonybest.com -- Sign up to Bryony's newsletter for rewards and exclusive discounts.

Twitter - @bryony_best

Instagram - @bestbryony

Facebook – The Girl from Pompey

Tik Tok - @bryonybest

Bryony Best

# AUTHOR BIO

Bryony Best was born and raised in Portsmouth, United Kingdom. Currently residing in Hayling Island with her fiancé and her much loved Chihuahua dog named Luna. Bryony works as a Holistic Therapist and lives a happy life of mindfulness and wellbeing. Bryony has previously published three memoir books, and her aim is to become a full time writer.

(The Girl from Pompey: Discovering the Key to Happiness and Fulfilment) Published - 2021

(The Girl from Pompey: Conversations with the Dead!) Published – 2022

(The Girl from Pompey: Bloodshed in the Hampshire Cabin) – 2023

Bryony drew on experiences from her life to write this book, and her inspiration to share her stories with the world is to shine a light on mental health, addiction and trauma healing. Since releasing her books, Bryony has been invited to facilitate talks for mental health and addictions within local schools and colleges, raising awareness for the younger generations.

NEVER GIVE UP!

Printed in Great Britain
by Amazon

28120881R00084